April '70

QUALITY CONTROL
and RELIABILITY

QUALITY CONTROL
and RELIABILITY

Practice-tested Methods and Procedures, based on Scientific Principles and Simplified for Immediate Application in a Variety of Manufacturing Plants.

Norbert Lloyd Enrick, Ph.D.

Associate Professor, Stevens Institute of Technology
Consultant in Quality Control and Reliability

FIFTH EDITION — SECOND PRINTING

INDUSTRIAL PRESS INC.

200 MADISON AVENUE, NEW YORK 10016

Library of Congress Catalog Number: 66-15790

PRINTED IN THE UNITED STATES OF AMERICA

FOREWORD

Managers, inspectors and engineers are vitally concerned with quality control and product reliability. For this purpose, many of them may wish to have a simplified but valid presentation of the subject, using practical illustrations from a variety of industrial applications. *Quality Control and Reliability* aims at this goal.

Modern quality control combines effective testing and inspection with statistical aids. For example, statistical methods permit sampling procedures that *minimize sampling risk* while at the same time maximizing the relative *quality protection* attainable. Or, as a further illustration, statistically established limits on control charts signal a warning when a production process has gone out of control. The prime emphasis of the book is on the *control of quality:* assurance of incoming materials, control during production, and checking of outgoing merchandise. Some years ago, a book might have been complete with this material. However, the advent of stringent long-term guarantees on many consumer items and the absolute need for proper functioning of space-age equipment has focused attention on a special facet of quality: reliability.

Product reliability refers to the probability that there will be no failures in performance, as in the case of a washing machine that should not need major repairs before the expiration of, say, 3 years, or an orbiting geophysical laboratory that is to collect and send information for a given period of time under expected environmental stresses. Several chapters deal specifically with the problem of assuring product reliability. While "reliability" is often denoted separately—as is done in the title of this book—a sound quality control program views reliability as an integral part of quality. For this reason, the word "quality" when used by itself may be presumed to include the concept of reliability.

Most of the case histories in this book come from the author's consulting experience, with the selection of individual examples guided by teaching experience in university and industrial training courses.

November, 1965
Hoboken, New Jersey   Norbert Lloyd Enrick

CONTENTS

PART I

Basic Quality Control Applications

1

Fundamentals of Inspection

To control the quality of manufactured products, three
methods of inspection are in use:

1. Screening
2. Lot-by-Lot Inspection
3. Process Inspection.

SCREENING

If every unit of product is inspected and the defective
ones are screened out, this is called *"screening"* or *100 per
cent inspection*. Screening is often preferred to any other
method of inspection because "only if you inspect every
piece can you be sure to catch all the defectives." However,
experience has shown that *100 per cent inspection does not
guarantee a perfect product*. The monotony of screening
inevitably creates fatigue and lowers attention. Therefore,
no inspector can ever hope to catch all of the defectives. He
always misses some and usually more than is anticipated.
If a perfect product is to be guaranteed, it will usually be
necessary to do at least 200 per cent inspection unless some
completely mechanical inspection device can be used.

In most types of mass production, screening can be used
only sparingly because it is expensive and time consuming
and interferes with the flow of work. Furthermore, there
are many types of "destructive" testing where 100 per cent
inspection would result in 100 per cent destruction of product. Examples are the sharpness testing of razor blades,
which dulls the edges; tensile strength tests of wire, which
snap the wire; chip tests of enamel which crack the enamel;

and firing tests of ammunition. With such products other methods of quality control are a necessity.

Screening is inevitable in the case of vital parts upon which the functioning of an entire assembly depends, and also where a process normally turns out a high percentage of defective product. An example of the latter case is the production of high precision ball bearings—a difficult process which normally results in 20 per cent unacceptable product. In inspecting end product prior to shipment to the customer, screening is generally the method of choice.

LOT-BY-LOT INSPECTION

Lot-by-lot inspection was invented to overcome the high cost of screening. A lot may consist of an accumulation of product, such as incoming material, partly finished articles and subassemblies, or completed product. Instead of examining each piece, the inspector limits himself to checking a relatively small number of sample pieces and then judges from them the acceptability of the whole lot.

The limitations of this procedure are that a sample does not always give a true picture of the entire lot from which it has been selected. *For example,* a lot may contain a great proportion of defectives, but since the inspector happens to pick up only good pieces in a small sample, he may erroneously accept the lot even though the lot as a whole is bad. On the other hand, a lot may contain only a very few bad pieces and yet these may be included in the inspector's sample, resulting in the unwarranted rejection of a good lot. These errors are known as *sampling errors* and are a familiar headache to experienced inspectors.

Here modern statistics of mathematical probability helps the inspector by furnishing him with ready made sampling plans that guarantee a *minimum amount of inspection for a maximum amount of protection* against sampling errors. How to achieve this is the main topic of the Chapter "Procedure in Installing Lot-by-Lot Inspection."

Without proper sampling plans, there usually will be either too much inspection or else not enough, resulting in excessive costs or ineffective control.

PROCESS INSPECTION

Process inspection is accomplished by an inspector who patrols an assigned area, checking up on equipment, methods of operation, and occasional pieces of product from raw material to finished article. The purpose of process inspection is to discover defective products where and when they occur, so that corrective action can be taken immediately. Process inspection is concerned with all causes of defective work, be it operator, operation, equipment or raw material.

The limitations of process inspection are that inspectors cannot be stationed at all machines at all times. As a result, considerable quantities of defective material may slip through between inspectors' visits. This applies especially to difficult control operations, such as precision machining, intricate casting, certain types of spot and resistance welding, and many chemical, mechanical and electrical measurements. In such cases, the roving inspector often finds the faulty operation only after the damage in the form of defective work has already been done.

From this experience the necessity arose to create methods which *show quickly when something is wrong or is about to go wrong with the process*, sometimes even before defective work makes its appearance. The most important achievement of the science of statistical quality control is to have developed such methods and to have brought them into a form which can be used easily without difficult mathematics. These methods are known as the *control chart system*, which is the main topic of Chapter 4 on "Installing Process Inspection."

WHEN NOT TO INSTALL STATISTICAL QUALITY CONTROL

You do not merely install quality control in a plant. The matter must be considered thoroughly in order to decide upon a plan. Such preliminary thinking may indicate that statistical quality control is not applicable to the majority of operations in your plant.

For example, if you are stamping out non-precision metal blanks on punch presses, it will be sufficient for the operator or foreman to give the product an occasional spot check for burrs and scorch marks. This will be sufficient to detect deficiencies in the blanking die or material and insure a satisfactory product. Generally speaking, any elaborate quality control is uncalled for on product or operations where all the following conditions exist:

1. The product is a non-precision product.
2. The quality of the product can be checked quickly.
3. Defective work is unlikely.

2

Procedure in Installing
Lot-by-Lot Inspection

Four steps are to be followed in setting up lot-by-lot inspection for a particular item:

Step 1: Set up Inspection Lots.
Step 2: Arrange for Rational Lots.
Step 3: Establish an Allowable Percent Defective.
Step 4: Select a Sampling Plan.

STEP 1: SET UP INSPECTION LOTS

Under lot-by-lot inspection, the size of the inspection lot may vary from about 300 articles up to any number. As will be shown, for lots smaller than 300 either process inspection or screening is preferable.

As a rule the quantity of product which normally moves through the shop in a single lot is also your inspection lot. *For example,* a hand-truck with two tote boxes, each containing 300 blanks, may be a practical lot in the press-working department. On the other hand, a barrel of 5,000 galvanized washers might be a practical lot in the plating department.

Theoretically, there is no upper limit to the size of the lot. But in practice lots should be kept small enough so that they are easy to move and do not require special handling.

Another factor influencing lot size is how frequently you wish to inspect the work from one machine. *For example,* a hammer is producing approximately 1,000 multiple die drop forgings per hour. You wish to inspect the work every half hour, so that if quality should go out of control you can detect it fairly soon; therefore the lot size should be approximately 500 each. In other words, small lots give you a better control over the process and prevent waste of materials; but it is not desirable to make lots *too* small. As a rule 300 pieces is the minimum size as previously mentioned. If production lots are smaller than 300, it is better to accumulate two or three of them until you have a sizeable inspection lot. You do not save much by sampling lots smaller than 300 and might as well do 100 per cent inspection on them, unless control charts (to be discussed later) can be used as an alternative.

STEP 2: ARRANGE FOR RATIONAL LOTS

A "rational lot" is one whose units have been produced from the same source. As much as possible, a lot should consist of articles produced from one batch of raw materials; one production line or machine; one mold, pattern or die; and one and the same shift. Often it is not possible in practice to separate product as strictly as that, but you should adhere to the rule of forming rational lots as closely as possible. If you mix up products from different sources and find a bad lot, you cannot put your finger immediately upon the source of trouble—which can be done if there are rational lots.

To illustrate, a die-casting department has three different tumbling barrels for washing and polishing small zinc castings. Lots are kept separate and a note on each route tag indicates in which barrel each lot has been tumbled. Now if the inspector finds a lot which contains too many chipped, broken or poorly polished castings, he can immediately locate the barrel in which the trouble occurred by merely referring to the route tag. On the other hand, if lots had been mixed up it would have taken much longer to find out which tumbling barrel was not working properly.

STEP 3: ESTABLISH AN ALLOWABLE PERCENT DEFECTIVE

The idea of an Allowable Percent Defective is arrived at from the following considerations: Under the speed of mass production, it is often impossible to continually turn out 100 per cent satisfactory product. One must assume that a certain percentage of defectives will always occur on certain processes; however, if the percentage does not exceed a certain limit, it is often more economical to allow the defectives to go through rather than to screen each lot. This limit is called the *Allowable Percent Defective.*

To illustrate, in a certain automatic polishing operation it was found that up to 1 percent defective pieces (incompletely polished) is not abnormal. It would have been rather expensive to screen each lot after polishing. Therefore it was decided to consider 1 percent the Allowable Percent Defective, even though this small quantity of bad material would go through to plating and finishing only to be thrown out in the final screening before shipment.

Second illustration: In a certain centrifugal casting operation, it was found that up to 2 percent of the work might normally be expected to be defective. Because of the high cost of further processing operations on this casting, it was determined that 2 percent defectives was not allowable. This meant that screening had to be installed.

Thus the principle of establishing the Allowable Percent Defective becomes apparent: As soon as you have determined the normal percentage defective which the particular operation produces, you have to ponder the important question: Is the normal percent defective produced *allowable* or *not?* If you have decided that it *is allowable,* then you should use a proper sampling plan to see that, in the *long run,* no more than the allowable percentage of defectives is passed even though some accepted lots have more than this. If you have decided that the normal percentage defective which the machine produces is *not allowable,* then you should install screening inspection on every lot. By doing so, you achieve two important objectives: You then make sure that no more than the allowable percentage of defectives goes through further production and you also know when something goes wrong with the process.

One question needs still to be answered: *How do we establish the normal percent defective?* To do this you have to watch the product for some time while it is under regular operation. Ordinarily, sufficient data can be accumulated over a period of one to two weeks to determine the percentage of defectives normally occurring in the product from certain equipment and operations. Already existing records of past performance are also a good guide in determining the capability of the machine.

To illustrate, records accumulated from inspection of product revealed the following percentages of defectives produced in one day on three 500-pound drop hammers:

	Hammer No. 1	Hammer No. 2	Hammer No. 3
Lot No. 1	2.0%	0.8%	1.9%
Lot No. 2	1.8%	1.3%	2.2%
Lot No. 3	1.3%	7.4%*	2.5%
Lot No. 4	1.1%	0.5%	0.8%
Lot No. 5	1.3%	1.2%	1.2%
Lot No. 6	1.8%	1.2%	1.2%
Lot No. 7	0.9%	1.4%	0.8%
Lot No. 8	4.7%*	0.9%	2.6%

The two percentages marked with an asterisk represent lots containing an unusually high portion of defectives. Investigation revealed faulty dies and failure to correct the set-up promptly as the causes of the poor quality. The percentages observed here were considered clearly abnormal. Most of the remainder of the lots showed defectives varying roughly between 1 and 2 percent, and considered normal. A few figures were somewhat above 2 percent, but in the absence of any demonstrable mechanical failure of the equipment, carelessness of operators had to be assumed as responsible.

Data, such as given above, were collected for several additional days to make sure that all normal operating conditions would be covered. Comparisons were made to analyze differences in scrap due to different operators and different dies. The final conclusion reached was that up to 2 percent defectives in any lot should be considered as not abnormal, and this figure was finally adopted as the Allowable Percent Defective.

The example presented indicates that a certain amount of judgment, rather than precise scientific measurements, will enter into determinations of the Allowable Percent Defective. The question is sometimes asked whether there are any standard tables furnishing definite values of the normal percent defective for various machines and operations. The answer is *no*. To initiate such a program of standard tables seems hopeless because account would have to be taken of such variables as age and condition of all types of equipment, differences in raw materials, skill of operation, degree of maintenance, and many other factors; therefore, it is still necessary to make individual determinations in each shop. Before any final decision is made on the choice of an Allowable Percent Defective, the inspection supervisor should consult the Engineering, Planning and Cost Departments of his plant.

As regards *incoming materials*, the Allowable Percent Defectives will depend upon commercial standards or your firm's own specifications. Incoming materials may be sampled statistically just as work in process or end product. Accordingly, many technical committees of manufacturers' associations are now establishing standards for Allowable Percent Defective in purchased materials and sampling plans to be used. Prominent in this field is the Radio Manufacturers' Association, whose committee recently recommended 1 percent as the Allowable Defectives in electron tubes. Individual large buyers, such as the U. S. Army and Navy's Procurement Divisions, several department stores, and manufacturing organizations often specify the Allowable Percent Defective right in the purchase order and inspect accordingly.

STEP 4: SELECT A SAMPLING PLAN

Let us assume that the Allowable Percent Defective on a certain item is established at 2 percent and that inspection lots consist of approximately 750 pieces each. If you want to make sure that in the long run, the average of defectives passed will not exceed 2 percent, you have to know:

1. How many sample pieces to inspect in each lot.
2. When to accept the lot.
3. When to reject the lot.

Table 1. Master Sampling Table

LOT SIZE	SAMPLE SIZE	ALLOWABLE PERCENT DEFECTIVE																													
		0.25		0.5		0.75		1		1.5		2		3		4		5		6		7		8		9		10		12	
		A	R	A	R	A	R	A	R	A	R	A	R	A	R	A	R	A	R	A	R	A	R	A	R	A	R	A	R	A	R
499 or less	40	→		→		→		0	2	0	2	0	3	1	4	1	4	1	6	2	6	2	7	3	7	3	8	4	9	4	9
	50	→		→		→		0	2	0	3	1	3	1	4	2	5	2	6	3	7	3	8	4	9	4	9	5	10	5	11
	60	→		→		→		0	3	1	3	1	3	2	5	2	5	3	7	4	8	4	9	5	10	5	11	7	12	7	13
	70	→		→		→		1	3	1	3	1	4	2	5	3	6	4	8	5	9	5	9	6	10	7	11	8	13	8	13
	80	→		→		→		2	3	3	4	3	4	4	5	5	6	7	8	8	9	8	9	9	10	10	15	12	13	12	13
500 to 799	40	→		→		*	*	*	2	0	3	0	3	0	4	1	5	1	5	1	6	1	7	2	8	2	8	2	9	4	10
	60	→		→		*	*	0	2	0	3	1	4	1	5	2	6	2	7	3	8	3	9	4	10	4	11	5	11	6	12
	80	→		→		0	1	1	3	0	4	1	5	1	6	3	7	5	8	5	10	5	11	6	12	7	13	8	14	9	15
	100	→		0	1	0	2	1	3	1	4	2	5	2	6	4	8	6	9	6	11	7	13	8	14	9	15	10	17	12	18
	120	→		0	2	1	3	2	3	3	4	4	5	5	6	7	8	7	9	11	11	12	13	13	14	15	15	16	17	18	19
800 to 1,299	40	→		→		*	*	*	2	*	3	0	3	0	4	0	5	0	6	1	6	1	7	1	8	2	8	2	8	2	10
	60	→		→		*	*	0	2	0	3	0	4	1	5	1	6	2	7	2	8	3	9	3	10	4	11	4	11	5	12
	80	→		→		0	2	0	3	1	4	1	5	2	6	3	7	3	8	4	10	5	11	5	12	6	13	8	15	8	15
	100	→		0	2	0	2	0	3	1	4	2	5	3	7	4	8	5	10	5	11	7	13	7	14	9	15	10	17	13	18
	120	→		0	2	1	3	1	3	2	5	3	6	4	8	6	9	6	11	7	13	8	14	9	16	11	18	12	19	16	21
	160	→		1	2	2	3	3	4	4	5	5	6	7	8	9	10	10	11	13	14	15	16	16	17	18	19	19	20	22	23
1,300 to 3,199	50	*	1	*	1	*	2	*	3	*	3	0	3	0	4	0	5	0	6	1	7	1	8	2	9	2	10	3	10	3	11
	75	*	1	*	1	0	2	0	3	0	4	0	4	1	5	2	7	2	8	3	9	3	10	4	12	5	12	6	14	6	15
	100	0	1	0	2	0	2	1	4	1	4	1	5	2	6	3	8	4	9	5	11	6	13	6	14	8	15	9	17	10	18
	125	0	1	0	2	1	3	1	4	2	5	2	6	3	7	4	9	5	11	7	13	8	15	9	16	11	18	12	20	13	21
	150	1	2	1	2	1	3	2	5	3	6	3	7	4	8	6	10	7	13	9	15	10	17	11	19	14	21	15	23	16	25
	200	2	2	1	2	2	3	4	4	5	5	6	7	8	9	10	11	13	14	17	18	18	19	20	21	22	23	26	25	27	28

A—Acceptance number; R—Rejection number; *No acceptance at this sample size.
Arrows: When there is an arrow under given "Allowable Percent Defective," use first sampling data below arrow. (Form larger lots if possible).

Table 1 (Continued) Master Sampling Table

ALLOWABLE PERCENT DEFECTIVE

LOT SIZE	SAMPLE SIZE	0.25 A	0.25 R	0.5 A	0.5 R	0.75 A	0.75 R	1 A	1 R	1.5 A	1.5 R	2 A	2 R	3 A	3 R	4 A	4 R	5 A	5 R	6 A	6 R	7 A	7 R	8 A	8 R	9 A	9 R	10 A	10 R	12 A	12 R
3,200 to 7,999	50	*	1	*	2	*	2	*	3	*	3	*	4	*	5	0	6	0	7	0	8	1	9	1	10	1	11	2	11	2	12
	100	*	1	*	2	0	3	0	4	1	4	1	5	1	7	2	8	3	10	4	12	5	13	5	15	6	16	8	17	9	19
	150	0	2	0	3	1	4	1	5	2	5	2	7	2	8	5	11	5	13	8	15	9	17	10	19	11	21	13	23	15	25
	200	0	2	1	3	2	4	2	5	3	6	3	8	4	10	7	13	8	16	12	19	13	21	15	24	16	26	19	29	21	31
	250	0	2	1	4	2	5	2	6	4	8	6	8	6	11	9	15	11	18	15	22	17	25	19	28	22	32	25	35	28	38
	300	1	2	3	4	4	6	5	6	7	8	8	9	10	11	15	16	17	18	22	23	25	26	29	30	32	33	36	37	39	40
8,000 to 21,999	100	*	2	*	3	*	3	*	4	*	5	*	6	0	8	1	9	1	11	2	12	3	14	4	16	5	17	←		←	
	150	*	2	*	3	0	4	0	5	0	6	1	7	2	9	3	11	4	14	5	15	6	17	9	20	10	22	←		←	
	200	0	2	0	3	0	5	1	6	1	7	3	9	3	11	5	13	7	17	9	19	11	22	13	24	16	27	←		←	
	250	0	2	0	4	1	5	2	6	2	8	5	11	5	14	7	16	10	19	13	22	15	25	18	29	19	32	←		←	
	300	0	3	1	4	2	6	2	7	3	9	6	13	8	16	11	18	12	22	16	26	19	29	22	33	24	37	←		←	
	400	1	3	1	4	3	7	4	7	5	11	10	18	16	23	16	25	18	27	22	34	27	37	31	42	34	47	←		←	
	500	2	3	3	4	6	7	7	8	9	11	14	18	22	30	22	33	28	29	34	35	40	41	45	46	50	51	←		←	
22,000 to 99,999	100	*	3	*	3	*	4	*	5	*	6	*	8	0	8	0	9	1	13	2	16	←		←		←		←		←	
	200	*	3	*	4	0	5	0	6	1	9	1	11	3	11	3	15	6	18	8	20	←		←		←		←		←	
	300	0	3	0	4	1	6	1	8	3	12	3	14	5	14	7	19	11	23	14	26	←		←		←		←		←	
	400	0	3	1	5	2	7	3	9	5	14	5	17	8	18	11	23	16	28	21	33	←		←		←		←		←	
	600	1	4	2	6	3	9	5	11	8	17	11	20	14	23	19	31	27	38	34	46	←		←		←		←		←	
	800	1	4	3	7	5	11	8	14	14	23	18	28	23	35	27	41	37	49	48	58	←		←		←		←		←	
	1000	3	4	6	7	10	11	13	14	24	25	30	31	31	46	40	52	53	54	65	66	←		←		←		←		←	
100,000 and up	200	*	3	*	5	*	7	*	8	0	9	0	13	2	13	2	18	←		←		←		←		←		←		←	
	400	*	4	0	6	0	8	0	10	3	12	3	17	7	18	9	25	←		←		←		←		←		←		←	
	600	0	4	1	7	2	10	2	12	5	15	7	20	12	22	17	33	←		←		←		←		←		←		←	
	800	1	5	2	8	4	11	5	14	8	18	11	24	18	29	24	40	←		←		←		←		←		←		←	
	1000	1	5	3	9	5	13	7	17	11	21	15	28	23	35	32	47	←		←		←		←		←		←		←	
	1200	2	5	3	9	7	14	9	19	14	24	22	34	32	40	39	55	←		←		←		←		←		←		←	
	1600	4	5	8	9	14	15	19	20	24	25	33	34	45	46	61	62	←		←		←		←		←		←		←	

Arrows: When there is an arrow under given "Allowable Percent Defective," use first sampling data above arrow.

This is simple. All the information is in ready made sampling plans, such as are supplied by the accompanying Master Sampling Table (Table 1).[1]

Example 1: *To illustrate,* let us assume that the Allowable Percent Defective for a certain metal stamping is 2 percent. Lot sizes consist of approximately 750 pieces each. To find the applicable sampling plan, the following method is used:

Step 1: The Master Table is entered under "Lot Size" for lots of 500 to 799. In the second column of this horizontal section are found the sample sizes: 40, 60, 80, 100, 120.

Step 2: Moving to the right, in the same horizontal section, to the column for 2 percent, the Acceptance and Rejection Numbers are obtained, thus for *A:* 0, 1, 1, 2, and 4; and for *R:* 3, 4, 5, 5, and 5.

Step 3: By combining these figures, the complete sampling plan is obtained:

Sample Size	Acceptance Number	Rejection Number
40	0	3
60	1	4
80	1	5
100	2	5
120	4	5

Now you start using the plan. Begin by selecting 40 sample pieces at random from different parts of the lot. If you find no defectives, accept the lot since the acceptance number is *0*. If you find 3 or more defectives, reject the lot, since the rejection number is 3. But what if you find 1 or 2 defectives? The defectives you have found lie between the acceptance and rejection numbers and you can neither accept nor reject the lot. The thing to do then is to gather additional evidence by taking another sample of 20 from the lot. This brings the total sample size up to 60 (40 plus

---

[1]The statistical basis of the sampling plans tabulated in this chapter is explained in Chapter 12.

20). Again compare the total number of defectives found up to this point to determine whether to accept or reject the lot or to continue sampling. This process may go on until the highest sample size is reached, 120, at which point the gap between the acceptance and rejection numbers disappears and the problem of acceptability is finally solved.

It should be understood that this sampling table has been set up on the basis of an *overall* percent defective, that is the final percent of defective parts that can be expected over a considerable run. This table therefore rests on the assumption that all rejected lots will be screened so that they become theoretically perfect and thus will raise the general average quality of the lots passing through.

In the particular case covered by Example 1, for instance, the acceptance number of 4 in a sample of 120 actually represents a maximum of $\frac{4}{120}$ or 3.3 percent defective, whereas the Allowable Percent Defective is only 2. Thus, occasionally individual lots having between 2 and 3.3 percent defectives will be passed through (not considering those bad lots which slip by now and then due to the "luck of the draw" errors normally present in the sampling process) although in the long run the overall proportion of defectives will be held at 2 percent. The probability of occasional errors of rejecting good lots and accepting bad ones is discussed in Chapter 12 with specific reference to the sampling plans given in Table 1.

Example 2. Let us assume that for another item usual lots sizes are approximately 3,000, and the Allowable Percent Defective is 1 percent. Then the following sampling plan is obtained from the Master Table by referring under "Lot Size" to lots ranging from 1,300 to 3,199.

Sample Size	Acceptance Number	Rejection Number
50	*	3
75	0	3
100	1	4
125	1	4
150	2	5
200	4	5

This particular plan differs from the one previously presented chiefly in the fact that it contains an asterisk in place of the first acceptance number. As indicated in the Master Sampling Table, an asterisk means no acceptance can be made at this sample size. In other words, you can reject a lot if you find three or more defectives in your first sample, but you cannot accept even if you find no defectives at all, because the sample size is too small. In the latter case, you have to examine an additional 25 articles, bringing your total sample size up to 75 (50 + 25). This new sample is sufficiently large to permit acceptance of the lot if no defectives have been found. In all other respects, you use this plan the same way as the one in the preceding illustration.

THE LEAST AMOUNT OF INSPECTION

The type of sampling just described is called *sequential sampling* because a sequence of samples is taken. You may ask: "Why bother with a sequence of samples? Are there no plans that require only one sample of definite size to make a decision?" There are such plans and they are known as *single sampling plans*. In such cases a Master Table of Single Sampling Plans (Table 2) is used. These plans are not so economical because sequential sampling usually requires much less inspection to determine the quality of any lot than single sampling plans.

At first glance, this statement may seem paradoxical, because in Example 1 we might have to inspect 120 pieces, but this is not likely to happen very often. As a rule a sample of 40 or 60, under the conditions of Example 1, would give the desired answer. If it occasionally happens that you have to do much additional sampling on any lot, this only proves that the lot was on the borderline between good and bad and really needed more sampling to arrive at the right decision. If a lot is *very good* or *very bad*, then usually the inspection of the first sample will give you the proper answer. In general, sequential sampling cuts inspection costs in half compared with single sampling.

A special type of sequential sampling is *double sampling*, developed by H. G. Romig and H. F. Dodge of the Bell Telephone Organization, and used widely throughout the Bell System and Western Electric.   Instead of providing for several sequential samples to be inspected. double sampling plans require only *two* samples.   Since the recently developed multiple sequential sampling plans save considerably more inspection than double sampling, double sampling plans have not been included in this treatise.

SINGLE SAMPLING vs.
SEQUENTIAL SAMPLING

Despite the fact that sequential sampling requires, on the average, only half as much inspection as single sampling, there are some plants where single sampling is still preferred.   The reason is one connected with material handling problems.   If the product is bulky and difficult to move, such as large castings, heavy coils, etc., it will be less costly to move a large number of sample articles to a place of inspection at *one time*, rather than to move a much smaller number of units *several times*.

HOW TO USE SINGLE SAMPLING PLANS

The application of single sampling is best illustrated by an example.   Let us assume that the Allowable Percent Defective for a certain item is 1 percent.   Each lot consists of approximately 300 units.   From the Master Table of Single Sampling Plans (Table 2) the individual sampling plan needed is selected as follows:

Step 1: The Master Table is entered in the horizontal section for lots of 499 or less.   In the second column of this section is found the sample size 75.

Step 2: Moving to the right in the same horizontal section to the column for 1 percent, the Acceptance and Rejection Numbers are found:

A	*R*
1	2

Table 2. Master Table of Single Sampling Plans

ALLOWABLE PERCENT DEFECTIVE (A—Acceptance number; R—Rejection number)

LOT SIZE	SAMPLE SIZE	0.25 A	0.25 R	0.5 A	0.5 R	0.75 A	0.75 R	1 A	1 R	2 A	2 R	3 A	3 R	4 A	4 R	5 A	5 R	6-7 A	6-7 R	8 A	8 R	9 to 12 A	9 to 12 R
499 or less	75	→	→	→	→	→	→	1	2	2	3	3	4	4	5	5	6	6	7	8	9	10	11
500 to 799	115	→	→	→	→	→	→	2	3	3	4	4	5	6	7	8	9	9	10	11	12	14	15
800 to 1299	150	→	→	→	→	1	2	3	4	4	5	5	6	8	9	10	11	12	13	15	16	20	21
1300 to 3199	225	→	→	1	2	2	3	4	5	5	6	8	9	11	12	14	15	17	18	21	22	29	30
3200 to 7999	300	→	→	2	3	3	4	5	6	7	8	10	11	14	15	18	19	22	23	26	27	←	←
8000 to 21999	450	1	2	3	4	4	5	6	7	9	10	14	15	20	21	26	27	←	←	←	←		
22000 to 99999	750	2	3	4	5	5	6	8	9	13	14	23	24	26	27	←	←						
100,000 and up	1500	3	4	6	7	8	9	13	14	23	24	←	←	←	←								

A—Acceptance number; R—Rejection number. "Allowable Percent Defective" use first sampling data below arrows in upper left-hand corner (forming larger lots if possible) or first sampling data above arrows in lower right-hand corner, as case may be.

Arrows: When there is an arrow below given.

Step 3: By combining these figures, the complete sampling plan is obtained:

Sample	Acceptance Number	Rejection Number
75	1	2

The plan is now ready for use. You simply inspect a sample of 75 pieces. If not more than one defective piece is found, accept the lot, since the Acceptance Number is 1. If you find two or more defectives, reject the lot, since the Rejection Number is 2.

For comparison, there is furnished below the particular sequential sampling plan corresponding to the single sampling plan. This comparison will show that while single sampling plans are simpler to apply, sequential sampling plans require much fewer articles to be inspected on the average; in fact a sample of 40 frequently will give the desired result. Again assuming a lot of 300 units and 1 per cent for the Allowable Percent Defective, we find in Table 1 the following:

Sample Size	Acceptance Number	Rejection Number
40	0	2
50	0	2
60	0	3
70	1	3
80	2	3

MEANING OF ARROWS IN MASTER SAMPLING TABLES

Acceptance and Rejection Numbers are not supplied in the upper left and lower right corners of Tables 1 and 2. Instead, these sections contain arrows pointing downward and upward respectively. The downward arrows indicate that sample sizes adjacent to arrows are not large enough and larger samples should be employed; the upward arrows indicate that smaller samples should be employed. This is illustrated by the following example:

Example 1:   For a certain item assume that the Allowable Percent Defective is 0.5 percent and the usual lot size is approximately 1,000.   *Find* a Single Sampling Plan for this item.

Procedure: Examination of the Master Table 2 discloses that no acceptance and rejection data are available for lots of 800 to 1,299 when the Allowable Percent Defective is 0.5 or less; instead there is an arrow pointing downward. This means that the next lower section of the table must be used.   This is the section under 0.5 for lots of 1,300 to 3,199, which is reproduced below:

Sample Size	Acceptance Number	Rejection Number
225	1	2

The procedure now is the same as described previously. Sequential plans are established in a similar manner.

Example 2:   As another illustration, assume that the lot size is 30,000 and 7 is the allowable percent defective; find a sequential sampling plan.

Procedure: By referring to Master Table 1 and the section for lot sizes of 22,000 to 99,999 an arrow under 7 pointing upward indicates that the data for lot sizes 8000 to 21,999 should be employed in this case.

RANDOM SAMPLING

Samples must be selected in a truly random manner from different parts of a lot.   This means that you should not examine locally as, for example, the top layer or the side layer of a lot, but should take samples at random.   In the long run this is the only method likely to minimize misleading results.   Hunting for defectives in the bottom corner of lots or any other such "systems" are not only ineffective but also defeat the primary purpose of sampling— to obtain a true representation of the lot as a whole.

MAJOR AND MINOR DEFECTS

In special cases it may be found desirable to use two different sampling plans for one item—one plan to control major defects and another plan to control minor defects. The latter plan would have a higher Allowable Percent Defective simply because the defects are of less importance.

To illustrate, in a particular type of stainless steel blanks, scale marks, die marks, and thick lines might be considered major defects with an allowable percent defective of 0.5 percent. At the same time, slight scratches, roll marks, light burrs, etc., might be considered minor defects with an allowable percent defective of 5 percent. Then the respective sampling plans are selected from the Master Table and used separately to accept and reject lots either on the basis of major or minor defects.

INSPECTION RECORDS

Once the sampling routine has been established, it is desirable that the inspector keep a lot-by-lot record of the lots inspected. Examples of such records are given in Figs. 1 and 2.

Inspection records should be submitted at the end of each day to the supervisor of inspection. Properly summarized they will give him a clear over-all picture of the daily manufacturing operations and enable him to put his finger on sore spots and advise the production, engineering and methods departments accordingly. In many plants, the standards department will use figures of inspection for establishing quality-quantity bonus systems.

ANALYSIS OF ENTRIES MADE ON
LOT-BY-LOT INSPECTION RECORD

On the record form presented in Fig. 1, there are shown entries covering lot-by-lot inspection for major and minor defects in six lots of small stainless steel parts following blanking operation. The particular entries made for each lot are analyzed in the following:

Lot No. 1001: The first sample of 40 blanks inspected

LOT-BY-LOT INSPECTION RECORD

1. ITEM: S. S. Part — Dwg. # 20999

2 LAST OPERATION: Blanking

3. OPERATOR: # 35

DATE OF INSPECTION			1/1	1/1	1/1	1/2	1/2	1/2
LOT NUMBER			1001	1002	1003	1004	1002R	1005
LOT SIZE			400	399	401	500	360	400
ORIGINAL OR RESUBMITTED LOT (Check One)			✔ ORIG. / RESUB.	✔ ORIG. / RESUB.	✔ ORIG. / RESUB.	✔ ORIG. / RESUB.	ORIG. / ✔ RESUB.	✔ ORIG. / RESUB.

MAJOR DEFECTS

SAMPLING TABLE FOR MAJORS / MAJOR DEFECTIVES

SAMPLE SIZE	ACC. NO.	REJ. NO.	NUMBER	NUMBER	NUMBER	NUMBER	NUMBER	NUMBER
40	0	2	1	3 x	0 ✔	0	0	0
50	0	2	1					
60	0	3	1					
70	1	3	1 ✔					
80	2	3						

TYPES OF MAJOR DEFECTS FOUND / MAJOR DEFECTS

	NUMBER	NUMBER	NUMBER	NUMBER	NUMBER	NUMBER
Scale marks	1					
die-mark		III				
thick lines			1			
pin holes			1			

MINOR DEFECTS

SAMPLING TABLE FOR MINORS / MINOR DEFECTIVES

SAMPLE SIZE	ACC. NO.	REJ. NO.	NUMBER	NUMBER	NUMBER	NUMBER	NUMBER	NUMBER
40	1	4	2	2	1 ✔	2	1	4 X
50	1	4	2			2		
60	2	5	2 ✔			3		
70	3	5				4		
80	4	5				4		

TYPES OF MINOR DEFECTS FOUND / MINOR DEFECTS

	NUMBER	NUMBER	NUMBER	NUMBER	NUMBER	NUMBER
Slight scratches, roll marks	1	1	1	IIII		1
burrs	1	II				
small pin holes (superficial)					1	III

LOT ACCEPTED OR LOT REJECTED (Check One)	✔ ACC. / REJ.	ACC. / X REJ.	✔ ACC. / REJ.	✔ ACC. / REJ.	✔ ACC. / REJ.	ACC. / X REJ.

SIGNATURE   J. Jones

Fig. 1. Lot-by-Lot Inspection Record Showing Major and Minor Defects after Blanking Operation.

showed 1 major defective (scale marks) and 2 minor defectives (1 scratch and 1 mark from the rollers feeding the steel coil into the blanking press). Scale marks tend to indicate improper processing, particularly in respect to pickling at the steel mill; however, in successive samples no additional defectives were found, and it was assumed that the one piece represented merely an isolated streak at the beginning of the coil. When 60 sample pieces had been inspected, the number of minor defectives found up to that point was still only 2, which was equal to the Acceptance Number for "minors." Therefore, the lot was accepted for minor defectives but the lot could not yet be accepted for major defectives, since the number of defectives found up to this point was 1 and the Acceptance Number 0. Therefore the inspector had to inspect an additional sample of

LOT-BY-LOT INSPECTION RECORD

1. ITEM: Cold Drawn Steel Bars #134, 1½" diam.

3. OPERATOR: J. Jones

2. LAST OPERATION: Temper

4. DATE OF INSPECTION			4/1	4/2	4/2	4/3	4/3	4/4
5. LOT NUMBER			H 114	H 115	H 116	H 117	H 118	H 119
6. LOT SIZE (NO. OF PCS. IN LOT)			c. 450	c. 450	485	500	450	480
7. ORIGINAL OR RESUBMITTED LOT (CHECK ONE)			✓ ORIG. / RESUB.	✓ ORIG. / RESUB.	✓ ORIG. / RESUB.	✓ ORIG. / RESUB.	✓ ORIG. / RESUB.	✓ ORIG. / RESUB.
8. SAMPLING TABLE			9. MAJOR DEFECTIVES					
SAMPLE SIZE	ACC. NO.	REJ. NO.	NUMBER	NUMBER	NUMBER	NUMBER	NUMBER	NUMBER
40	0	2	0	1	4	0	0	0
50	0	2		1				
60	0	3		1				
70	1	3		1				
80	2	3		2				
CHECK NO.								
10. TYPES OF DEFECTS FOUND			11. DEFECTS					
			NUMBER	NUMBER	NUMBER	NUMBER	NUMBER	NUMBER
Handling marks				1	1			
scale					11			
laps					1			
bent				1				
12. LOT ACCEPTED OR LOT REJECTED (CHECK ONE)			✓ ACC. / REJ.	✓ ACC. / REJ.	ACC. / ✓ REJ.	✓ ACC. / REJ.	✓ ACC. / REJ.	✓ ACC. / REJ.

13. INSPECTOR'S SIGNATURE: K. Smith

Fig. 2. Lot-by-Lot Inspection Record of Cold-Drawn Steel Bars.

10, bringing the total sample size up to 70. Since no additional defectives were found, and the new Acceptance Number was 1, the lot could be accepted for "majors." Thus, the lot passed the standards for both major and minor defects.

Lot No. 1002: This lot revealed three major defectives in the first sample of 40, in addition to two minor defectives. Since for sample size 40 the Acceptance Number is 2 and the defectives found were 3, the lot was rejected. The die, which had begun to throw burrs and die-marks, was sent to the tool room for sharpening.

Lot No. 1003: This lot was produced on another die. It could be accepted for both "majors" and "minors" on the first sample size.

Lot No. 1004: This lot was accepted for "majors" on the first sample size; however, several minor defects were found, which called for additional inspection. The lot was accepted for "minors" only after a total of 80 sample pieces had been examined.

Lot No. 1002R: Lot No. 1002 had been rejected. Now it was resubmitted to the inspector as Lot 1002R, after having been screened. It was accepted on the first sample size.

Lot No. 1005: This lot was rejected on the first sample size, because the sample showed it contained too many minor defects in the form of scratches and pin holes. The existence of the great number of pin holes led to a further investigation and rejection of three coils of steel from a particular shipment, since similar surface imperfections were evident.

Note: In actual practice the inspector will rarely encounter the variety of defects shown in the specimen inspection record discussed here. These have been purposely increased in order to demonstrate all possible types of situations that may arise in the systematic application of sampling plans. As soon as a lot has been rejected, the foreman should be notified so that he can check into the trouble and correct the faulty operator, operation or equipment that may be responsible for the bad lot. Thus lot-by-lot inspection renders a most important service to the shop: it arrests immediately the flow of bad product and permits remedy before materials and time are needlessly wasted.

DISPOSITION OF DEFECTIVE MATERIAL

If incoming materials are inspected and the lot is found to be unsatisfactory, its disposition is a matter of special concern to the purchasing department and production superintendent. If a lot consisting of work in process or completed product is rejected, it may be submitted to screening to take out all the defectives, or it may be sent directly to repair and salvage, sold as seconds, or be scrapped entirely, whichever procedure involves the least loss.

Note: A special set of single, double, and sequential sampling plans is provided in Military Standard 105-A, published for the Department of Defense by the Government Printing Office. These plans are more elaborate and complex than those presented in this Chapter, and prior to using the Military Standard, it will be desirable to study Chapter 12 on "Statistical Basis of Modern Quality Control" in this book. Use of the Government plans is often prescribed when producing to Government contracts. In place of the term "Allowable Percent Defective," Military Standard 105-A uses the term "Acceptable Quality Level," which is defined as "a nominal value, expressed in terms of percent defective, specified for a given group of defects of a product." The two terms, "Allowable Percent Defective" and "Acceptable Quality Level" are thus equivalent.

3

Sampling Continuous Products

Continuous items of product, in contrast to individual units of product, consist of an uninterrupted length of material, such as belting, cloth, wire, cord, metal coil and long tubing. These items often require a considerable amount of visual examination for defects. Since we do not have individual sample pieces, a length of one yard is arbitrarily taken as the equivalent of a unit of product in applying the sampling tables. But here we face a practical difficulty. It is impracticable to select *at random* individual lengths of one yard from different parts of several long rolls. The frequent rolling, unrolling and marking off of sample yards is simply unworkable. Therefore, the following procedure is indicated: 1. Inspect continuous lengths of 50 to 75 yards each time. 2. Select these lengths from different parts of the lot.

Example: A lot consists of 15 rolls of wire strand, each 500 yards long. The total lot size is therefore 7,500 yards. This calls for a sample size of 525 yards as shown by Table 3. While the table shows sample sizes ranging from 525 to 1,275 for lot sizes of 9,999 or less, inspection begins with the smallest sample size, as previously explained.

Select one sample roll at random from the lot and inspect a continuous length of 75 yards near the beginning of the roll and 75 yards in about the middle of the roll. Then select another sample roll. This time inspect 75 yards about 1/3 way up the roll and 75 yards near the end of the roll. This process continues until the entire 525 sample yards have been inspected.

SPECIAL SAMPLING TABLES

In the procedure just given, it is evident that *the principle of random sampling is not completely adhered to;* consequently the usual sampling tables are no longer adequate, because they are constructed on the assumption that each

Table 3. Master Sampling Table for Continuous Items of Product

LOT SIZE, YARDS	SAMPLE SIZE, YARDS	ALLOWABLE PERCENT DEFECTIVE																								
		2		3		4		5		6		7		8		10		12		15		17½		20		25	
		A	R	A	R	A	R	A	R	A	R	A	R	A	R	A	R	A	R	A	R	A	R	A	R	A	R
9,999 or Less	525	11	21	16	28	22	36	26	42	32	49	37	55	42	62	53	74	63	86	78	106	92	120	106	135	131	164
	675	15	25	22	34	29	43	36	52	43	60	50	68	57	77	71	92	95	108	104	132	122	150	140	169	173	206
	900	22	32	31	43	41	55	51	67	60	77	70	88	79	99	98	119	117	140	144	172	167	195	191	220	237	270
	1125	29	39	41	53	53	67	65	81	77	94	89	107	102	122	121	142	148	171	183	211	213	241	243	272	301	334
	1275	38	39	53	54	69	70	83	84	95	96	112	113	126	127	154	155	181	182	222	223	257	258	291	292	360	361
10,000 to 24,999	600	12	23	18	31	24	39	30	47	36	54	42	62	48	69	60	83	72	97	90	118	105	135	119	152	150	186
	825	18	29	27	40	36	51	44	61	53	71	61	81	69	90	87	110	104	129	128	156	151	181	170	203	212	248
	975	23	34	33	46	44	59	54	71	64	82	74	94	84	105	105	128	124	149	155	183	180	210	205	238	255	291
	1275	31	42	46	59	59	76	73	90	87	104	100	120	113	134	141	164	167	192	207	235	240	270	272	305	339	375
	1500	43	44	61	62	78	79	95	96	103	104	129	130	144	145	178	179	211	212	258	259	300	301	337	338	418	419
25,000 to 49,999	675	13	25	20	34	26	43	33	51	41	60	47	60	54	76	67	92	81	108	101	131	118	150	135	170	168	208
	900	19	31	29	43	38	55	47	65	57	76	66	87	75	97	93	118	112	139	140	170	163	195	185	220	230	270
	1200	28	40	41	55	53	70	66	84	79	98	91	112	104	126	128	153	153	180	190	220	223	255	252	287	312	352
	1500	36	48	53	67	68	85	85	103	101	120	117	138	133	155	163	188	195	222	241	271	282	314	320	355	396	436
	1800	50	51	72	73	91	92	112	113	132	133	151	152	172	173	211	212	254	255	307	308	356	357	402	403	499	500
50,000 and Up	825	17	30	25	40	34	51	41	60	50	71	58	80	67	90	83	110	100	128	124	157	146	179	165	203	218	249
	1125	25	37	37	52	50	67	60	79	72	93	83	105	95	118	118	145	141	169	175	208	205	238	232	270	289	330
	1425	33	45	48	63	65	82	79	97	94	115	108	130	124	147	153	180	182	210	226	259	263	296	298	336	351	392
	1725	41	54	60	75	81	98	97	116	116	137	133	155	152	175	188	215	224	252	277	310	322	355	365	403	453	494
	2025	56	57	79	80	105	106	126	127	148	149	169	170	192	193	236	237	278	279	345	346	397	398	450	451	556	557

individual sample piece has been taken *at random* from different parts of the lot.

To compensate for the deficiency in random sampling of continuous items of product, the sample size has to be enlarged; how much is shown in Table 3 for sequential sampling and in Table 4 for single sampling. The method of establishing individual sampling plans from these tables is similar in principle to that given for Tables 1 and 2.

Table 4. Master Single Sampling Table for Continuous Items of Product

LOT SIZE	SAM-PLE SIZE	ALLOWABLE PERCENT DEFECTIVE												
		2		3		4		5		6		7		8
		A	R	A	R	A	R	A	R	A	R	A	R	A	R
9,999 or Less	675	22	23	30	31	38	39	46	47	53	54	62	63	70	71
10,000 to 24,999	825	25	26	36	37	45	46	55	56	65	66	74	75	83	84
25,000 to 49,999	900	27	28	38	39	49	50	59	60	70	71	80	81	90	91
50,000 and Up	975	30	31	41	42	53	54	64	65	74	75	85	86	97	98

LOT SIZE	SAM-PLE SIZE	ALLOWABLE PERCENT DEFECTIVE											
		10		12		15		17½		20		25	
		A	R	A	R	A	R	A	R	A	R	A	R
9,999 or Less	675	84	85	100	101	121	122	140	141	158	159	195	196
10,000 to 24,999	825	101	102	120	121	146	147	169	170	191	192	235	236
25,000 to 49,999	900	110	111	129	130	158	159	183	184	207	208	256	257
50,000 and Up	975	119	120	139	140	171	172	197	198	223	224	276	277

4

Installing Process Inspection

When processes and operations are difficult to control, the best means of process inspection is by means of the control chart. The primary purpose of control charts is to show trends in dimensional or other values toward whatever maximum and minimum limits mark the dividing lines between acceptable and defective products. While these control charts also show when the established limits have been exceeded, their main purpose is to provide means of anticipating and correcting whatever causes may be responsible for defective products. Thus, the fundamental principle relates to the prevention of defective work rather than a mere correction or cure after the defects occur. The working of a control chart is best understood by studying first simple charts.

GRAPHIC RECORD OF TESTS

Example 1: Fig. 3 presents a graphic record of Rockwell hardness tests of shovel blades. It is important that the hardness of these blades be closely controlled, since a soft blade will bend and a hard and brittle blade will break in use. For this reason the engineer has specified hardness to be within 45 ± 3 hardness numbers, Rockwell C scale. This means that the desired hardness for each blade is 45, but that blades measuring 48 or 42 are still inside the specification limits.

Each plotted point on the chart indicates the hardness reading of a shovel blade. Notice that the four pieces in a sample usually do not all have the same readings. *For*

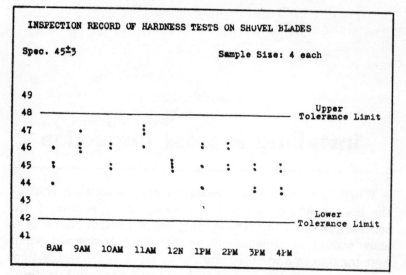

Fig. 3. Graphic Inspection Record of Hardness Tests on Shovel
Blades. Each Plotted Point on the Chart Indicates the Hardness
of a Blade.

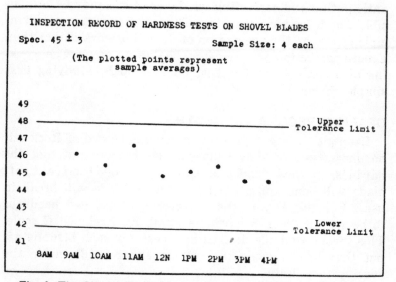

Fig. 4. The Shovel Blade Hardness Test Readings are Simplified
on This Chart by Plotting Only One Point for Each Sample of
Four Blades (the "Sample Average") instead of One Point for
Each Blade in a Sample, as in Fig. 3.

example, the first sample of four pieces showed the following degrees of Rockwell hardness: 46, 45, 45, 44. Typical causes of such variations follow. When the blades are in the furnace, they may not all be exposed to exactly the same amount of heat; they may not all be kept there exactly the same length of time; there may be variations in the metal itself. In addition there are slight variances in pressure used in testing each blade. The result is *variation*, both in the lot and in the sample.

If we were not dealing with a furnace but with a precision machine, we would still have tool wear, play in bearings and cams, maladjustments in setting, and atmospheric conditions which would cause variation. These are familiar causes. Of course there are many processes that are so uniform that the variation in them is of no practical significance. For those processes control charts are not needed. An occasional spot check is sufficient.

PLOTTING SAMPLE AVERAGES

In order to simplify the readings on the chart (Fig. 3) it is customary to plot just one point, for each sample of four blades, instead of one point for each blade in a sample. this point is the *sample average*. Thus, instead of plotting the points 46, 45, 45, 44 for our first sample, we just plot one point, 45. This point represents the average hardness. It is obtained by adding up the test results (46 + 45 + 45 + 44 = 180) and dividing the total by the number of pieces in the sample (180 ÷ 4 = 45). When the averages are plotted, the new chart will appear as shown in Fig. 4.

Example 2: Suppose we had been inspecting small compression springs made on a spring coiling machine and were testing the free length of each spring. Assume that its first sample consists of five pieces, measuring respectively 1.01", 1.02", 1.03", 1.02", 1.03". Here again the sample average is obtained in the same manner as previously explained.

1st sample piece....... 1.01"
2nd sample piece....... 1.02"
3rd sample piece....... 1.03"
4th sample piece....... 1.02"
5th sample piece....... 1.03"
_____
Total .... 5.11"
Average .... 1.022" (5.11 ÷ 5).

1.022" or, rounded cut, 1.02" is the average free length of the five sample units—the sample average.

These charts of averages lead easily into our main topic: control charts.

CONTROL CHARTS

Fig. 5 shows the same chart as Fig. 4 with the exception of two dotted lines which have been added. They are the *control lines* or *control limits* and their presence makes the chart a *control chart.*

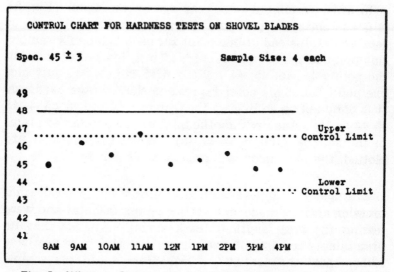

Fig. 5. When a Chart such as the One Shown in Fig. 4 is Supplemented by Adding Control Lines or Control Limits (See Dotted Lines), it Becomes a "Control Chart."

The control lines form a narrower band than the specification limits. If we were to demand that all the product should fall within this narrower band, this would be equivalent to more exacting demands on the process than indicated by the tolerance specification. This is not the intention and all the product within the tolerance limits still is acceptable. However, *we draw certain conclusions if a sample average should fall outside the dotted control lines.*

WHAT THE CONTROL CHART TELLS US

Let us again look at the chart, Fig. 5. Most of the time the plotted points which represent sample averages are well within the control limits; but in one sample, the one taken at 11:00 A. M., the plotted point fell outside the control limits—*a maverick!*

A maverick has only one significance: something has probably gone wrong or is about to go wrong with the process and a check is in order to prevent the appearance of defective product. The cause of the trouble may be simple. In our example of blades it may be a maladjustment of the furnace heat, improper timing, carelessness, or inferior metal.

If the cause has been eliminated, the following plotted points will stay well within the control limits; but if more "mavericks" appear, then a very thorough investigation should be made, even if it is necessary to shut down production temporarily until everything is adjusted again and no more mavericks appear.

MACHINE SHOP APPLICATIONS

Another useful example of the many applications of the control chart can be taken from certain types of turret lathe, grinding and similar machine shop processes. In some cases, operators change tools too often and make unnecessary adjustments, whereas others run the machines too long without tool sharpening or operate them carelessly. The remedy is the control chart *right at the machine*. It tells the operator:

1. When plotted points are inside control limits, tool and machine adjustments are correct.
2. When a "maverick" appears, change tools or adjust machine accordingly.

Additional examples of quality control charts for different types of processes are given in Figs. 6 and 7.

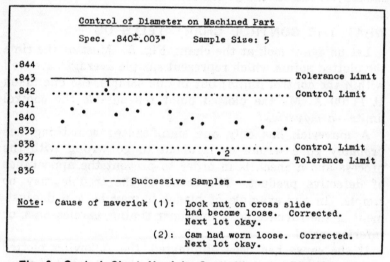

Fig. 6. Control Chart Used in Controlling the Diameter of a Machined Part.

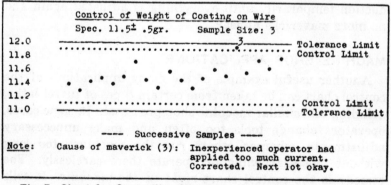

Fig. 7. Chart for Controlling Weight in Connection with a Wire Coating Operation.

Now it becomes clear why we are using control limits that are closer than the requirements of the tolerance. These limits are designed to enable us to detect trouble in the process even before any damage in the form of defective product has occurred.

If a sample average falls outside the control limits, it rings a warning that the process is out of control. If a sample piece falls outside the specification limits, it indicates that defective product has already occurred.

PROCESS VARIABILITY

You cannot locate control lines without knowing about the variability of the process. The idea of process variability is derived from the following consideration. No process can turn out an identical product. Even with the best equipment and the most skilled operation, no two pieces will be *exactly* alike. This fact reflects the variability of the process. We cannot eliminate this natural variability, but we can try to keep it within the requirements of the specification limits.

How variability is measured may be demonstrated from the example of hardness tests on blades. Let us say that in the first sample of four pieces tested, you obtained the hardness readings of 46, 45, 45, 44, Rockwell C scale. The difference between the highest test result, 46, and the lowest test result, 44, is 2. This difference of 2, in our example, is called the *sample range*. You repeat this procedure of obtaining the sample range on the next 9 samples (or more) and you get the test results here tabulated (see tabulation headed "Example of Computation of Process Variability"). The total of the sample ranges is 16. Divide this total by the number of samples, 10, and you get 1.6. This 1.6 is the value representing the *process variability*. As a general rule 10 samples are sufficient in estimating process variability; however, if a high degree of accuracy is essential, up to 20 samples are required.

Now draw two lines, one 1.6 hardness numbers below the upper specification limit and the other 1.6 above the lower specification limit. The new lines are the control limits, and the chart is ready for use. The importance of control charts in process inspection is further illustrated by Fig. 8, which indicates how the quality of a lot is directly affected by the variability of the process.

EXAMPLE OF COMPUTATION OF PROCESS VARIABILITY

Quality Characteristic Tested: Rockwell Hardness of Shovel Blades

Test Results

Sample No.	First Blade Tested	Second Blade Tested	Third Blade Tested	Fourth Blade Tested	Sample Range
		Rockwell Hardness—C Scale			
1	46	45	45	44	2
2	46	47	46	46	1
3	45	45	46	46	1
4	46	45	45	45	1
5	46	47	47	45	2
6	46	46	47	47	1
7	46	48	47	45	3
8	45	46	44	45	2
9	45	46	46	45	1
10	46	47	46	45	2
—				TOTAL....	16

$$\frac{\text{Total of Sample Ranges}}{\text{Total Number of Samples}} = \frac{16}{10} = 1.6$$

This average of 1.6, also called Average Range, is the value representing the Process Variability.

ROUTINE OF SETTING CONTROL LIMITS

To facilitate routine computation of control limits, the steps involved in the example just given would be:

Step 1: From a series of samples, the process variability is computed to be 1.6.

Step 2: Since the specification reads 45 ± 3 hardness numbers, as measured on a Rockwell C Scale, the upper and lower specification limits are 48 and 42.

Step 3: The control limits are now found as follows:

Upper Control Limit
48 minus 1.6 = 46.4

Lower Control Limit
42 plus 1.6   = 43.6

Step 4: Draw the two control limits, 46.4 and 43.6, on a control chart, as shown in Fig. 5. The chart is now ready for use.

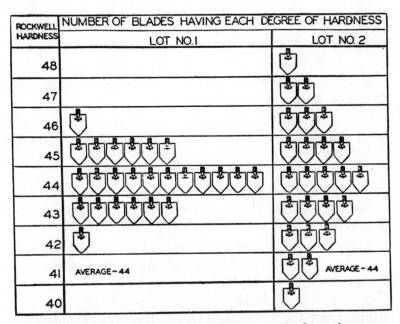

Fig. 8. These Two Lots of Shovel Blades have the Same Average Hardness but the Lots Differ as to Quality. Lot No. 1 is Superior to No. 2 Because It has Less Variability or "Spread." This Illustrates the Importance of Determining the Process Variability in Establishing Control Charts.

LIMITATIONS OF METHOD OF COMPUTATION

The method for computing control lines furnished here applies to samples of size 3, 4 or 5 each. For most purposes, these are the sample sizes recommended as practical. If different sample sizes are to be used, a numerical adjustment (as tabulated below) must be made in determining the value of the Process Variability *before* drawing control lines. This listing includes also slight adjustment factors for samples of size 3, 4 or 5, which may, however, be disregarded in practice. They are furnished for use where greater accuracy is desired.[1]

Sample Size	Multiply Process Variability by
2	1.5
3	1.1
4	1.0
5	0.9
6	0.9
8 to 10	0.8

When computing the process variability, certain rules should be observed.

Rule 1: Compute the process variability from only 10 to 20 of the last samples, each sample being taken from one lot. If the process is a continuous one, then each sample should represent a definite time interval, such as samples taken about every hour or half hour.

Rule 2: All samples should consist of the same number of pieces.

Rule 3: Any sample taken from an abnormally poor lot is obviously not representative of the normal process and should be omitted from the computations.

Once a process variability and control limits have been established on a particular process, they are generally useful for several weeks or even months. Occasionally they

---

[1] The derivation of these factors is shown in Chapter 13, but need not be known for practical applications. A more specic term for Process Variability is "Average Range."

should be recomputed to make sure that the process has not undergone any changes in the course of time.

MULTI-DIMENSIONAL OPERATIONS

There are many processes where more than one quality characteristic may require control, such as multi-dimensional operations on a turret lathe. Of course it would involve too much time and figure work to have a control chart for each of a multitude of characteristics on just one item of product. In such cases you have to confine yourself to the one or two most important characteristics—the ones that are most difficult to control. As to the other characteristics, subject them to occasional spot checks so that nothing is left completely to chance.

The limitation of control charts to only the most important quality characteristics of an operation has proven itself sound in practice. Usually it is found that if the difficult dimensions are under control, the remainder are similarly in line. There is a certain amount of interdependence when machining to dimensions.

SAMPLING LAST WORK PRODUCED
BEFORE INSPECTION

Lot-by-lot inspection requires that samples must be selected at random from all parts of a particular lot. However, under process inspection, which is primarily concerned with control of continuous runs of production rather than separate lots, the rule of random sampling does not apply rigidly. Instead it may be equally feasible or even better to take workpieces directly from the machine, such as a sample of four units produced just prior to the inspector's arrival. This method has the advantage of furnishing the *latest information* about the quality of the process from the *last work* produced, which is of great importance in detecting any impending trouble.

Here, of course, it is essential to use only the last regular workpieces and to guard against samples "stacked" in advance with only the best units. Neither should the sample represent work produced in the inspector's presence. These are points which will require consideration in each case. Once a decision has been made to perform last-work sampling or random sampling, it should be adhered to consistently. If you desire to change from one method to the other, it will be necessary to recompute the control limits, because a different variability factor is involved.

FURTHER CONTROL CHARTS

The type of control chart just presented has been selected as one of the simplest and most widely applicable. However, additional charts may be required, such as the range chart to be described in the next chapter. Also, in Part II of this book, still other types of control charts are described.

The type of chart just presented is known as a "control chart for averages," because it is used to plot sample averages. If we want to be still more specific, we should also state that the control limits are computed with reference to the specification limits or product tolerances. Thus we would call it a "control chart for averages" with "modified control limits."

Sometimes we may be called upon to install control charts on processes where tolerance limits have not been established. Then we should either establish such limits along the lines recommended in Chapter 9, or else we may use control limits computed with reference to the average level of the process, as explained in Part II, Chapter 15.

5

Special Control Charts for Old and Worn or Highly Variable Equipment

Occasionally it may happen that the method of control charts for sample averages, as just presented, does not yield satisfactory results. This occurs where equipment is old and machine parts are worn or out of alignment; or where processing is inherently quite variable. The product turned out under such conditions is not likely to be very stable or uniform and there is a constant possibility that variability may undergo sudden and unexpected increases.

Here there is need for an additional and more sensitive chart, the *control chart for ranges* or briefly the *range chart*. The purpose of the range chart is to permit constant vigilance over the variability of the process. For, as was demonstrated by Fig. 8, even though the average of a process may be perfectly centered about the specified dimension, excessive variability will result in inferior product.

Application of the range chart is called for if, after using a control chart for sample averages for some time, it is found that it frequently or occasionally fails to indicate trouble promptly. The range chart does not replace the sample average chart, but merely supplements it with additional information about the production process.

To illustrate, let us assume that variability on a screw machine operation has suddenly increased because of a loose cam. The *average* dimension of the product is still acceptable, but the *individual parts* vary so greatly that some of them begin to fall outside the specification limits. The control chart for sample averages may not yet indicate any trouble, but the range chart will—because it is especially designed to detect unusual variability.

The field of usefulness of range charts is not confined to occasional control of old and worn equipment. High precision processes whose variability must be carefully held within prescribed limits are best controlled by keeping a range chart in addition to the regular sample average chart. Similarly, many electro-chemical processes such as plating and micro-chemical-biological production, such as fermentation of yeast and penicillin, often call for application of range charts no matter how perfect the equipment, because unusual variability is quite inherent in such processes.

CHARACTERISTICS OF RANGE CHART

The range chart is similar to the sample average chart. Its distinguishing feature is a control limit for ranges. If a sample range (or difference between the highest and lowest value for a given sample) is plotted on this range chart and falls outside the control limit, it is an indication that the variability of the process has become excessive and corrective action is needed.

In Fig. 9 an example is furnished of a range chart used to control variability on a centerless grinding operation. When this chart was first introduced, many sample ranges were found to fall outside the control limit. This condition prevailed for some time, and although each lot produced showed a high percentage of defectives upon subsequent 100 percent inspection, nothing could be found wrong with the equipment. The frequency of wheel dressings was increased, but no improvement resulted. Thereupon an investigation was made of the diameter of the work being fed into the machine, which showed that it did not generally come in a very satisfactory condition from the preceding turning operation. Excessive variability of the turned parts going into the centerless grinder was established as the cause of the trouble. Following installation of control charts on the turning operation, the centerless grinding was likewise brought under control, as evidenced by the chart. For several lots thereafter, all sample ranges were well within

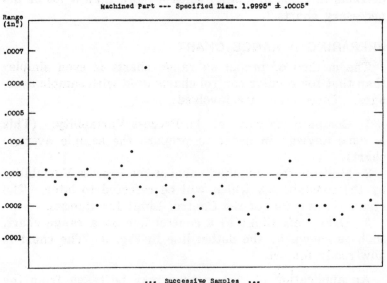

CONTROL CHART FOR RANGES
Machined Part --- Specified Diam. 1.9995" ± .0005"

Fig. 9. Example of a Range Chart Used to Control Variability on a Centerless Grinding Operation.

the control limit with the exception of one range. Subsequent investigation revealed that a loose slide on the grinding machine needed tightening.

After a range chart has been maintained for some time, it will frequently lead to the location and elimination of the sources of excessive variability. In the example just presented, lack of proper uniformity of the material going into production was detected as the cause and eliminated. At other times, the range chart will supply evidence that a more regular schedule of equipment maintenance should be adopted. Prior to the plotting of a range chart, these needs are often not recognized clearly enough to obtain prompt action. Once the primary sources of variability have been found and eliminated, the range chart should likewise disappear, since it is no longer needed. As the supervisor of a large electron tube shop explained: "We are careful to keep range charts only where they are needed. Nothing detracts interest in quality control more than a lot of unnecessary charts."

PREPARING A RANGE CHART

The method of preparing range charts is even simpler than that for regular control charts used with sample averages. Three steps are involved:

1. Compute the value of the Process Variability. (This is done anyway in order to prepare the sample average chart).

2. Multiply the computed value of the Process Variability by the constant 2.3 which will be referred to later. The result is the value of the Control Limit for Ranges.

3. Draw this Limit as a control line on a range chart, such as shown by the dotted line in Fig. 9. The chart is now ready for use.

An application of this method may be taken from the control of variability on the centerless grinding operation previously referred to. The operation is that of grinding cylindrical parts to a specified outside diameter of 1.9995 ± .0005 inch.

Step 1: From a series of sample results, the Process Variability has been computed to be .00013 inch.

Step 2: Multiplying .00013 inch by the constant 2.3 we obtain 0.000299 or nearly 0.0003 inch. This is the value of the control limit.

Step 3: The value of the control limit is used to draw a control chart for ranges, such as shown in Fig. 9.

When computing range control limits, the value of the Process Variability is always multiplied by the constant 2.3, as in Step 2 of the procedure just given. There are, of course, certain numerical adjustments that must be made on the Process Variability prior to computing control limits, *if the sample size is different from 3, 4 or 5,* and this has been explained under the heading "Limitations of Method of Computation" in Chapter 4. As a rule, however, sample sizes 3, 4 or 5 are the best and most widely used, and with them no numerical adjustments of the Process Variability are required.

The constant 2.3 is a value which results in range control limits corresponding closely to those furnished by the American Standards Association in Standard Z 1.3—1942. Statistical computations have shown that range control limits based on this constant, result in a very small chance—only about 5 in 1,000—of an erroneous indication of excessive variability in the process, when actually no such variability exists. In daily inspection, various inaccuracies and other practical limitations may result in a greater probability of error; however, that does not detract seriously from the value of the range control chart.

USING THE RANGE CHART

The range control chart is generally used in conjunction with an ordinary chart for control of sample averages. Therefore, the same test data used for the averages chart can also be used for plotting the range control chart. The steps involved are reviewed below:

1. Obtain the individual measurements from each sample. (Compute the sample average for the control chart for averages.)

2. Find the range of each sample average.

3. Plot each range on the range control chart. (This value should be plotted immediately after the sample average has been drawn in on the control chart for averages.)

Now watch the control charts. Whenever either a sample average or a sample range goes out of control, take appropriate action in notifying the production personnel concerned.

6

Applying Quality Control in the Plant

Once the method and principles of applying statistical quality control are understood, the next step is to try them out in the plant.

THE PILOT RUN

Do not attempt to introduce the system all over the shop simultaneously. Select one spot in production which appears most promising for success and let it be the starting point. Only after this "pilot installation" is operating properly should you extend it gradually to other machines and operations, production lines and departments, and finally the entire plant.

The proof of each installation lies in the results it yields. To make sure that it will be practical and workable, many quality control operators prefer to make a trial run first. Occasionally this may show that a tolerance, control limit, or Allowable Percent Defective needs adjustment; but sometimes all adjustments will prove unsuccessful. Then you may be confronted with one of those rare occurrences where the routine methods of statistical quality control are inadequate. For them the science of mathematical statistics has developed more sensitive and refined methods of analysis and control, which cannot be dealt with in this simplified treatise, and in such cases you may have to call in a consultant.

STARTING POINTS

When surveying the plant for quality control possibilities, you might look for the following points in production as the most promising:

1. Wherever screening is in use, investigate whether it cannot be replaced by the more economical sampling plans.

2. Examine "trouble spots" which are known to be producing too many defectives. They might be improved or eliminated by installing control charts.

3. Scrutinize points where superficial inspection or none at all is in use. If anywhere defectives are going through, they may be arrested by installing sampling plans.

TYPES OF INSPECTION IN DIFFERENT PRODUCTION STAGES

1. *Incoming Materials:* Many plants have either no inspection of incoming materials at all or else just a perfunctory examination. Here a study is indicated to determine through lot-by-lot inspection whether the material going into production conforms to quality standards. In other plants, where screening has been applied in the past, it may be found that it can be replaced by the more economical lot-by-lot inspection.

2. *Partly Finished Product:* This inspection involves the examination of product while it goes through its various productive stages. There may be certain operations on which defective work is difficult to avoid. Here a control chart or sampling plan will be of service. Which of the two may be preferable will be discussed after considering End-Product.

3. *End-Product:* When end-product or final product is inspected, screening is found to be the most widely prevalent method. As a rule it should not be replaced with any other method. However, if all preceding production operations have been brought under good control and very little defective product is "slipping through," screening of end-product may become superfluous.

CONTROL CHARTS vs. SAMPLING PLANS

To control the quality of work in process, we might either install control charts at the machine or inspect the product by means of a sampling plan. The question arises: Which method is preferable?

Many processes can be controlled successfully by either method. As a matter of fact, different plants use different methods on the same product with equal results. *For example:* A certain shaft is required to be machined to a diameter of 3 inches $+ 0.0000 - 0.0015$ inch. One plant uses a control chart, measuring each sample of four shafts and plotting the average on the chart. The other plant uses a sampling plan, checking each shaft with a "Go Not-Go" gage, and rejecting any lot where the sample indicates it contains too many defectives. Both plants are achieving satisfactory results; but this does not apply to all processes. In each individual case a decision has to be made on the basis of the following facts:

1. The information obtained from control charts is superior to the one obtained from sampling plans, because control charts often sound a warning when a process is going out of control even before defective product occurs. A sampling plan can only tell you that the process is out of control after the defectives have already been produced.

2. The sample size is much smaller under the control chart system, but sometimes each sample has to be tested very carefully in order to obtain a precise measurement or pointer reading. Sampling plans, although they require larger sample sizes, involve merely a simple test or visual examination to determine whether each item is satisfactory or defective.

3. The amount of figure work to be done is, of course, greater when the control chart is used, since we have to compute sample averages and process variability.

The advantages versus disadvantages are as follows:

	Advantages	Disadvantages
Control Charts	Superior Information	More Figure Work
	Small Samples	More Painstaking Tests
Sampling Plans	Less Figure Work	Less Information
	Simple Tests	Bigger Samples

It should be realized that in practice there are many examples where one of the advantages or disadvantages outweighs all the rest. *To illustrate:* When inspecting chrome plated items, it would be highly impractical to attempt to measure the brightness of finish along a numerical scale. Therefore it is preferable to classify each article "satisfactory" or "defective" and use a sampling plan. On the other hand, when determining yield point and elongation of steel castings, testing is so difficult, costly and time consuming that it is of primary importance to have small sample sizes. Here the control chart method must be used.

THE HUMAN FACTOR IN INTRODUCING QUALITY CONTROL

Installation of quality control is not only a technical problem, it is also a problem of human relations. As is only too well known to any quality control engineer, one of the most frequent causes of failure is the resistance built up by the shop man against the outside engineer who has come to establish the new method. Resistance to change is, after all, a normal human reaction. It may be aggravated by fear of loss of standing or even of losing one's job, by suspicion or simple stubbornness. Much time may have to be invested in tactful diplomacy to overcome this resistance.

In dealing with this phase of quality control, the inside inspection supervisor is in a far better position than the outside engineer. The former not only knows his men, machines and product, but has already had an opportunity to gain the confidence of both foremen and operators. This will prove helpful when he begins with his new project; moreover he is not pressed constantly for time in completing his task, but the outside man, as a rule, is expected to show results quickly.

7

Tolerances and Allowances in Interchangeable Manufacture

It will be evident to all who have read the preceding chapters that quality control conforms to the principle that "an ounce of prevention is worth a pound of cure." The purpose of mere inspection is to *find* defective products. The object of quality control is to minimize the production of defective work and at the same time improve the general average of quality. This is done, as previously pointed out, by establishing a systematic inspection procedure which shows definite trends toward whatever dimensional or other boundary lines lie between acceptable and defective products.

Now one very important application of statistical quality control is in the interchangeable manufacture of machines or other mechanical devices; in fact, quality control offers unusual economic advantages in many branches of the machine-building and metal-working industries. For this reason, some of the essential elements in machine-building practice which are allied closely to quality control will be outlined briefly in this chapter.

INTERCHANGEABLE MANUFACTURING AND ITS ADVANTAGES

The term "interchangeable manufacture" generally indicates that mechanical products are formed of parts made to whatever degree of accuracy is required to insure the proper functioning of any part in any one of a number of duplicate machines, even when parts are selected at random and regardless of the lot to which they belong or when they were made. Strict interchangeability, however, may not always be feasible and under practical working conditions

there are modifications of this system or different degrees
of interchangeability.

The interchangeable manufacturing system serves to
produce duplicate mating parts sufficiently accurate or uniform in size to insure assembling (at random) and proper
functioning without fitting individual parts together; however, in some cases each part may be made to fit any mating
part in a limited series, but this is not true interchangeability. In other cases, parts are assembled without fitting
but not until they have been selected so that each mating
pair has the desired fit. Thus, companion or mating parts
which happen to be made to the extreme limits of the allowable size, are not supposed to interchange, in many cases,
if assembled at random; consequently, *selective assembly*
is necessary. To illustrate, a shaft of maximum diameter
may not assemble in a hole of minimum diameter and such
a combination, or one close to it, is likely to occur whenever
parts are assembled at random; but by selective assembly
suitable fits may be obtained. This method is a modification
of interchangeable manufacture. Most mechanical devices
which are supposed to be interchangeable have some parts
which are strictly interchangeable and others which must
be selected to obtain proper fittings.

The chief advantage of interchangeable manufacture is
in the increase in manufacturing efficiency and resulting
reduction in manufacturing costs. When duplicate parts
of a mechanical device are sufficiently accurate to permit
interchangeability, the ease with which broken parts may
be replaced is another advantage, but is decidedly secondary
when compared with the reduction in costs.

DETERMINING DEGREES OF ACCURACY
REQUIRED FOR DIFFERENT MACHINE PARTS

In this mechanical age, machines and other mechanical
appliances are used for so many different purposes that
great accuracy is required in producing some of them and
comparatively little accuracy in producing others. Then,
too, different classes or qualities of fits are needed even
between parts of the same device to insure proper function-

ing. For instance, some assembled mating parts may require very tight fits, others fits which are not tight but are close enough to eliminate play or clearance, and still others which have a certain amount of clearance. The fundamental reason for such variations relates to the general purpose of the machine or other device, its quality, and the function of each part or group of parts entering into its construction. To illustrate the matter of function, a shaft in one case must revolve freely in a bearing but possibly with no appreciable amount of play. In another case, play is not objectionable. Then there are very tight fits, as illustrated by a plug or pin which is somewhat larger than the hole to receive it, so that in some cases tons of pressure are required to obtain a rigid and fixed assembly of the parts. Numerous other variations might be cited, all of which are related in the last analysis to the function of the part or parts. This means that the fits between assembled parts must be based either upon data established for similar applications or upon experience and judgment until more definite information is available. The question of fits leads to a very important point which will now be considered.

GENERAL METHOD OF SPECIFYING FITS
OF THE REQUIRED QUALITY

When a given class or quality of fit is known to be satisfactory, the next step is to provide means of obtaining it in a systematic way in the normal course of manufacturing practice. To take a concrete illustration, suppose that a certain fit is required between a cylindrical pin and a hole. It is evident that obtaining the desired fit necessitates some method of controlling the accuracy of both pin and hole and this leads us to the general and very important subject of *tolerances*.

First, we are confronted by the fact that absolute accuracy is impossible. Moreover, the closest possible approach to it would be very costly but in machine-building practice varying degrees of inaccuracy may be allowed or tolerated without impairing the function or practical usefulness of the machine or of the individual parts which form it. For example, suppose that experience with a given machine indicates that a certain shaft having a nominal diameter of 1 inch will function properly with a diameter variation anywhere, say, between 1 inch and 0.995 inch. Permitting this allowable error or tolerance of 0.005 inch instead of aiming for perfection, may mean the difference between economical manufacturing practice and an utterly impractical condition. So, in economical manufacturing the following steps are essential:

(1) Certain classes of fits between mating parts of a mechanical device are established.

(2) The kind or quality of fit is based upon proper functioning of the mating parts and of the entire mechanism. The durability of the device, as well as its initial performance, usually would be an important factor in determining what constitutes proper functioning.

(3) The relation between a given quality of fit and proper functioning may have been established by repeated performances of the same or similar apparatus. If such tested fit data are lacking, then experience and judgment must be relied upon because the tolerances and resulting allowances which determine fits cannot be established by employing fixed rules or formulas. In case the machine is an entirely new type, designers must rely as far as possible upon their experiences with other jobs that are closest in their approach to the one at hand.

(4) The different parts of a machine, especially if quite a number are required in its construction, have different classes of fits and degrees of accuracy because of the various functions.

(5) In machine-building practice, the range of allowable fits, and also of allowable errors in manufacturing, is quite large because mechanical devices in general vary from those which must be very precise to those which may be crude and inaccurate without impairing their usefulness.

(6) Fits even for work intended to be of the same class or quality must vary to some extent because variations are inherent in all manufacturing processes; but by controlling

them so as to avoid errors too large to permit proper functioning of the part or parts, great manufacturing economy is effected.

(7) The quality of a fit and permissible variation depend upon fixing whatever maximum and minimum limiting dimensions will give the desired quality, but since the dimensions of acceptable parts vary and may lie anywhere between the extreme limits allowed, the fits vary accordingly as, for example, when the fits are between pins and holes or other internal or external parts.

(8) After the tolerance has been established for a given part, thus fixing certain minimum and maximum limits to the over-all dimensions, means should be provided in the regular course of manufacture to maintain these limiting sizes. To this end control charts, with limits based upon both the tolerances for a given part and the variability of the production process, are finding increasing application because of their efficiency and economy.

HOW VARIABILITY OF PRODUCT AFFECTS FITS BETWEEN MATING PARTS

Since small dimensional variations within the allowable limits are to be expected, it is evident that there will be corresponding variations in the tightness or looseness of fits between mating parts such as the fit of a shaft in the hub of a gear or pulley. To illustrate, if a shaft of the maximum allowable diameter should happen to be assembled in a hole of the minimum allowable diameter, the tightest fit would be obtained. If these conditions were reversed and the minimum shaft were assembled in a maximum hole, then the loosest fit would be obtained. Suppose as an example of fit variation, we take the case of a cylindrical part having a maximum diameter of 2 inches and a minimum diameter of 1.9995 inch. Assume that this part is to fit into a hole having a minimum diameter of 2 inches and a maximum diameter of 2.0008 inches. In this case, the maximum shaft and minimum hole are the same size, but if a minimum shaft happens to be assembled in a maximum hole there will be a clearance of 0.0013 inch. One might wonder if such minimum or maximum fit values would always be acceptable. The answer is *no* in many cases where unusual precision or uniformity of the fittings is essential. This point will be considered later.

BASIC DIMENSIONS

A basic dimension or size may be defined as a theoretical size to which a tolerance is applied in order to obtain a degree of accuracy which meets practical requirements or is within *allowable* minimum and maximum limits. Now when maximum and minimum limiting dimensions have thus been established for some part, the basic size may either be the minimum or the maximum and it may also, in some cases, be between (usually midway) the maximum and minimum limiting dimensions. If the basic size is the minimum, then the tolerance is plus relative to it; if the basic size is maximum, the tolerance is minus relative to it; and if the basic size lies between the maximum and minimum dimensions the tolerance is divided, equally as a rule, so that it is both plus and minus relative to basic.

If the basic diameter of some cylindrical part is, say, 2 inches and the tolerance is $+ 0.0000$ and -0.0005, then the allowable range of sizes is from the maximum diameter of 2 inches down to the minimum diameter of $2 - 0.0005$ $= 1.9995$ inch. If the hole for this cylindrical part has a basic size of 2 inches and the tolerance is $+ 0.0008$ and $- 0.0000$, the allowable range of hole sizes is from 2 up to 2.0008 inches. As a general rule, the minimum diameter of a hole is its basic size. In the case of a mating shaft, the maximum diameter usually is the basic size.

Before dealing further with the relation between basic dimensions and tolerances, it might be well to mention that the American Standard for Preferred Limits and Fits for Cylindrical Parts includes a *preferred series* of basic sizes or diameters. This series (see accompanying Table 5) ranges from 0.010 up to 21 inches. The object of a preferred series of basic sizes is to reduce the number of diameters commonly used in a given size range.

Table 5. American Standard Preferred Basic Sizes

...	0.0100	...	...	.....	0.80	5½	5.5000	5.5
...	0.0125	...	⅞	0.8750	...	5¾	5.7500	5.75
1/64	0.015625	...	...	.....	0.90	6	6.0000	6.0
...	0.0200	...	1	1.0000	1.0	6½	6.5000	6.5
...	0.0250	...	...	.....	1.1	7	7.0000	7.0
1/32	0.03125	...	1⅛	1.1250	...	7½	7.5000	7.5
...	0.0400	0.04	...	.....	...	8	8.0000	8.0
...	0.0500	...	1¼	1.2500	1.25	8½	8.5000	8.5
...	.....	0.06	1⅜	1.3750	...	9	9.0000	9.0
1/16	0.0625	...	...	.....	1.40	9½	9.5000	9.5
...	0.0800	...	1½	1.5000	1.50	10	10.0000	10.0
3/32	0.09375	...	1⅝	1.6250	...	10½	10.5000	10.5
...	0.1000	0.10	1¾	1.7500	1.75	11	11.0000	11.0
⅛	0.1250	...	1⅞	1.8750	...	11½	11.5000	11.5
...	.....	0.15	2	2.0000	2.0	12	12.0000	12.0
5/32	0.15625	...	2⅛	2.1250	...	12½	12.5000	12.5
3/16	0.1875	...	2¼	2.2500	2.25	13	13.0000	13.0
...	.....	0.20	2⅜	2.3750	...	13½	13.5000	13.5
¼	0.2500	0.25	2½	2.5000	2.5	14	14.0000	14.0
...	.....	0.30	2⅝	2.6250	...	14½	14.5000	14.5
5/16	0.3125	...	2¾	2.7500	2.75	15	15.0000	15.0
...	.....	0.35	2⅞	2.8750	...	15½	15.5000	15.5
⅜	0.3750	...	3	3.0000	3.0	16	16.0000	16.0
...	.....	0.40	3¼	3.2500	3.25	16½	16.5000	16.5
7/16	0.4375	...	3½	3.5000	3.5	17	17.0000	17.0
½	0.5000	0.50	3¾	3.7500	3.75	17½	17.5000	17.5
9/16	0.5625	...	4	4.0000	4.0	18	18.0000	18.0
..	.....	0.60	4¼	4.2500	4.25	18½	18.5000	18.5
⅝	0.6250	...	4½	4.5000	4.5	19	19.0000	19.0
11/16	0.6875	...	4¾	4.7500	4.75	19½	19.5000	19.5
...	.....	0.70	5	5.0000	5.0	20	20.0000	20.0
¾	0.7500	0.75	5¼	5.2500	5.25	20½	20.5000	....
						21	21.0000	...

RELATION BETWEEN TOLERANCES AND BASIC DIMENSIONS

If all of the tolerance is in either a plus or a minus direction relative to a basic dimension, the tolerance is known as "unilateral" because it is in one direction. For example, if a shaft diameter is 2 inches + 0.0000 — 0.0005, the tolerance of 0.0005 is minus and unilateral. If the tolerance is divided relative to a basic dimension, it is known as "bilateral." For example, if the center-to-center distance between two holes is given as 6 + 0.003 — 0.003 or 6 ± 0.003 inches, this indicates that the tolerance may be either plus or minus 0.003 inch and it is known as "bilateral."

Unilateral tolerances are recommended usually for mating surfaces such as fits between internal and external cylindrical or other parts. However, when the parts are tapering in form, the tolerance may be unilateral in some cases and bilateral in others. If the variation in the position of, say, a taper plug in a hole, is less likely to cause trouble in one direction than in the other, then the tolerance should be unilateral and either plus or minus. If a minus tolerance will tend to locate the plug away from the preferred direction, obviously the tolerance should be plus. If a variation in either direction is equally objectionable, then the tolerance should be divided and bilateral. The center-to-center distances between holes usually are bilateral because ordinarily a variation in either direction is equally objectionable. The center-to-center distance between the bearings for gears, however, represent one exception. In this case, the tolerance should be unilateral and plus because a slight increase in the center-to-center distance is not likely to cause trouble but a decrease in center distance might result in excessive pressure between the teeth and cause unsatisfactory operation.

RELATION BETWEEN TOLERANCE AND ALLOWANCE

Tolerance or allowable error should not be confused with *allowance* which indicates the difference between the dimensions of mating parts. An allowance is intended to provide whatever fit or degree of tightness or looseness may be required between the assembled parts. If the internal member, such as a cylindrical pin or shaft, is somewhat smaller than the external member, such as the hub of a lever, pulley or gear, then the allowance represents *clearance*. On the contrary, if the internal member is larger than the external part, the allowance represents *interference of metal;* consequently, the parts must be assembled either (1) forcibly, as in a hydraulic press; (2) by heating the outer member and thus expanding it enough to permit assembly; or (3) by cooling the inner member by means of dry ice or liquid nitrogen, thus contracting it enough to permit assembly.

The actual allowance is affected by the actual tolerances

and resulting sizes of both hole and shaft. To illustrate, assume that a pin has a maximum size of 4 inches and a tolerance of $+ 0.0000 - 0.0006$. If we assume that the hole to receive this pin has a minimum size of 4 inches and a tolerance of $+ 0.0010 - 0.0000$, the minimum allowance would be zero and the maximum allowance 0.0016 inch. These variations in allowances and resulting fits are due to the fact that the actual tolerances on mating parts may vary from zero up to the maximum and these variations occur in connection with both internal and external members; consequently, allowances between assembled parts may vary considerably and the extremes occur when a maximum pin and minimum hole or minimum pin and maximum hole are assembled together.

Now, if the need for tolerances could be entirely eliminated and if every part could be made to an exact dimension, it is evident that allowances for fits could be absolutely uniform. But tolerances are essential; hence, where variations in fit allowances must be exceptionally small there are two possible methods of procedure. One method is to reduce the tolerances, but if the reductions are excessive it may not be possible to utilize standard manufacturing equipment, or, in fact, any kind that would not result in prohibitive manufacturing cost. A second method of securing tolerance uniformity and often the only economical one, is to produce the parts efficiently and without attempting to secure such exceptional accuracy that special methods are required, and then select or sort them so that extreme size and allowance variations are avoided. This method of "selective assembly," as it is called, is to insure assembling those parts which, as a result of selection, are known to have the required allowance. This selection or sorting of groups according to size is sometimes done automatically by utilizing automatic gages or gaging machines which are now available in various forms. Automatic gaging may be employed either to detect parts which are not within the maximum and minimum limits or the apparatus may be designed for the more complete operation of selecting parts into a number of groups according to their sizes, as in selective assembly. The latter method is commonly employed in size grouping such parts as anti-friction bearing balls or rollers.

STANDARDIZATION OF TOLERANCES AND ALLOWANCES

The great importance of tolerances and allowances in the manufacture of mechanical devices has resulted in the adoption of standards for the general guidance of those who specify these dimensional values (these standards will be found in engineering handbooks). Previously, there was reference to American Standard Preferred Basic Sizes. Since preferred tolerances and allowances are a logical complement to preferred sizes, a series of tolerances and allowances has been included in the American Standard. This

Table 6. American Standard Preferred Series of Tolerances and Allowances

0.1	0.3	0.7	1.2	2	3	5	9	16	25	40
0.15	0.4	0.8	1.4	2.2	3.5	6	10	18	28	45
0.2	0.5	0.9	1.6	2.5	4	7	12	20	30	50
0.25	0.6	1	1.8	2.8	4.5	8	14	22	35	60

All dimensions are given in thousandths of an inch.

series is listed in Table 6. The total range, as the table shows, is from 0.0001 to 0.0600 inch. The purpose of this series is to reduce, as far as possible, the total number of different tolerances needed to meet practical requirements. In this Standard series there are only forty-four tolerances between .0001 and .0600 inch. When the engineer or designer specifies tolerances taken from whatever part of this Standard series meets his requirements, he avoids using a lot of tolerance values which are in between and therefore differ from the Standard series but have no practical advantage over this series.

The American Standard for Preferred Limits and Fits for Cylindrical Parts provides a table showing ten tolerance grades for cylindrical parts of from 0.04 to 200 inches in diameter. These tolerance grades are taken from the series in Table 6. Based on the ten tolerance grades just described, the American Standard provides data for various classes of fits which may be obtained by the application of these tolerance grades. These various classes of fits were designed on a unilateral hole basis and are described in the following section. It should be noted that the fits described include all of those which appear in the recommendations of the American-British-Canadian Conferences recommendations for sizes up to 20 inches diameter.

CLASSES OF FITS FOR CYLINDRICAL PARTS

The American Standard B4.1—1955, Preferred Limits and Fits for Cylindrical Parts, provides a number of classes of fits ranging from running and sliding to force and shrink fits. These fits, designated as RC, LC, LT, LN, or FN, provide standard limits for hole and shaft for a series of size ranges extending, in some cases, from .04 to 200 inches. The limits are selected so that the fit obtained by mating parts in any one class will produce approximately similar performance throughout the size ranges.

The following classes of running and sliding fits are provided: Class RC 1 Close Sliding Fits are intended for accurate location of parts which must assemble without perceptible play; Class RC 2 Sliding Fits intended for accurate location but with greater maximum clearance than Class RC 1; Class RC 3 Precision Running Fits are about the closest fits which can be expected to run freely (these are intended for precision work at slow speeds and light journal pressures) ; Class RC 4 Close Running Fits are intended chiefly for running fits on accurate machinery with moderate surface speeds and journal pressures, where accurate location and minimum play is desired; Classes RC 5 and RC 6 Medium Running Fits are for higher running speeds, or heavy journal pressures, or both; Class RC 7 Free Running Fits are intended for use where accuracy is not essential, or where large temperature variations are likely to be encountered; and Classes RC 8 and RC 9 Loose Running Fits are intended for use where material such as cold-rolled shafting and tubing made to commercial tolerances are involved.

Locational Fits include: Class LC Locational Clearance

Fits intended for parts which are normally stationary but which can be freely assembled or disassembled; Class LT Locational Transition Fits which are a compromise between clearance and interference fits, for application where accuracy of location is important, but either a small amount of clearance or interference is permissible; and Class LN Locational Interference Fits which are used where accuracy of location is of prime importance and for parts requiring rigidity and alignment with no special requirements for bore pressure.

Force Fits include: Class FN 1 Light Drive Fits which require light assembly pressures and produce more or less permanent assemblies; Class FN 2 Medium Drive Fits which are suitable for ordinary steel parts or for shrink fits on light sections. Class FN 3 Heavy Drive Fits which are suitable for heavier steel parts of for shrink fits in medium sections; and Classes FN 4 and FN 5 Force Fits which are suitable for parts which can be highly stressed or for shrink fits where the heavy pressing forces required are impractical.

UNIFIED AND AMERICAN STANDARD
FOR SCREW THREADS

This important standard provides several classes of external and internal screw threads which may be combined in various ways to obtain a number of different fits. Thus, there are Classes 1A, 2A, and 3A external threads and Classes 1B, 2B, and 3B internal threads. Classes 1A and 1B have the widest tolerances and Classes 3A and 3B the narrowest. In addition, the older Classes 2 and 3 for both external and internal threads have been retained from the former American Standard. Although most frequently, a Class 1A external thread will be used with a Class 1B internal thread, a Class 2A external thread with a Class 2B internal thread, and so on; actually any class of external thread: 1A, 2A, 3A, 2, or 3 may be combined with any class of internal thread: 1B, 2B, 3B, 2, or 3 to obtain the kind of fit desired.

Since interchangeable manufacture is applied extensively in mass production, its economic importance is apparent.

It is also evident that this system of manufacture is based upon the application of suitable tolerances and allowances; consequently precise means of checking dimensions are required to see if they are within the maximum and minimum prescribed limits. This checking involves the use of various forms of gages and measuring instruments. The inspection data obtained in this manner may be used in turn to review and revise tolerances in order to obtain limits which are close enough to guarantee proper functioning of the article and which are yet as liberal as permissible in order to maintain economical production. These matters are discussed in the next two chapters. Scientific quality control is a modern and valuable adjunct to the mere checking of finished products because it represents scientific inspection applied far enough in advance of defective production to prevent it or at least hold it within reasonable bounds.

8

Mass Production Gaging

Control of dimensions of product, such as width, length and diameter, requires the use of many types of measuring equipment. The simplest instrument for this purpose is the steel rule, which permits fairly reliable measurements to within 1/100th of an inch. This accuracy is usually not sufficient, and in order to obtain greater precision calipers are generally used. A common caliper, the micrometer, permits direct readings up to 1/1000″, with readings to 1/10000″ when equipped with a vernier scale. For still greater precision, dial gages, precision gage blocks, electronic gages, compressed air, and optical devices may be used.

When large quantities of product are to be inspected, it is of advantage to use gages which have been made or adjusted to the limits required so as to permit quick checks of product for conformance to the required dimensions. Considerable ingenuity has been developed by engineers in designing gages for checking various classes of dimensional errors.

LIMIT GAGES

In interchangeable manufacturing, various types of gages must be employed to check the linear dimensions, angular dimensions, amount of taper, roundness, concentricity, parallelism, and contour, as, for example, the involute form of a gear tooth. Thus, interchangeable manufacturing depends not only upon tolerances but also upon precise and efficient measuring or gaging devices for checking whatever tolerances have been established. It is impracticable, however, within the scope of this treatise to describe and illustrate the important types of gages and gaging machines because this subject alone would require

61

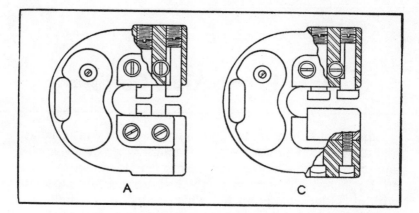

Fig. 10. Two Forms of American Standard Limit or "Snap" Gages. This Form of Gage Shows if Parts are within the Maximum and Minimum Limiting Dimensions.

a large volume. But a few limit gages of standard design will be referred to, partly to illustrate the relation between limits and the general principle of limit gaging.

The limit gage is a very common type and, as the name implies, it shows whether the size of a part is within the allowable maximum and minimum dimensions, but the fixed limit gages do not show the actual size. One form of limit gage which is commonly used for external measurements is shown at *A*, Fig. 10. This gage and the other examples of gage design here illustrated conform to the American Standard. The gage illustrated at *A* has two sets or pairs of measuring pins. If the work is within the allowable limits, it will pass between the first pair but not between the second pair. This explains why a gage of this general type is often referred to as "Go" and "Not Go" or as "Go" and "No Go." Model *C* is shown at the right in Fig. 10. It has two flanged gaging pins or "buttons" and a single block anvil opposite.

At *A* in Fig. 11 is shown a common type of limit gage for holes. The "Go" end at the left is longer than the "Not Go" end at the right so that the user can distinguish readily between the two. The gage illustrated at *B* is known as a "progressive" type. The "Go" and "Not Go" sections are

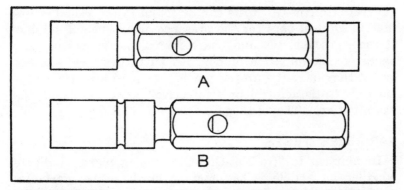

Fig. 11. Two Forms of American Standard Limit Gages for Holes.

combined in a single unit and the minimum allowable diameter is followed by the "Not Go" end. According to the American Standard, Type *A* is for diameters ranging from .059 to and including 1.510 inches, whereas the progressive Type *B* is for diameters from .240 to 2.510 inches.

The advantage of "Go Not-Go" or limit gages is that they permit the inspector to determine quickly whether or not a particular dimension of an article falls within the prescribed limits without the labor of adjusting or reading a measuring instrument. The limits of such a gage are, of course, those given by the tolerance.

While fixed limit gages simplify the work of the inspector, they are not desirable on precision processes where it is also important to know *how far* or *to what degree* a product is inside or outside the tolerance. Knowledge of this degree of variation often furnishes important information on how and where equipment needs adjustment. An ordinary limit gage can only be used to indicate whether an article *does* or *does not* conform to specified tolerances. No attention is paid to the degree of deviation from the specification.

It is important to note that from the special use of limit gages just referred to, the term "Go Not-Go" or "Go No-Go" testing has been adopted to cover all types of inspection that determine whether some product is, or, is not satisfactory, conforming or non-conforming, regardless of the degree of variation from the specifications. Examples of such general "Go Not-Go" tests can be found in the visual examination of steel bars for the presence or absence of sulphur stringers, scabs, pit and chafe marks, heavy seams, and bends; or examination of polished parts to check whether or not they have the proper finish. Articles are either considered "satisfactory" or "defective" as a result of the examination. They either "Go" or do "Not Go."

VARIABLES TESTS

In contrast to "Go Not-Go" tests which merely indicate whether an article is satisfactory or defective, variables tests also indicate the *degree* of deviation. This may be shown either in inches, pounds, Rockwell units, or whatever other scale is applicable for the particular product and quality characteristic.

To illustrate, the ultimate shear strength of certain spot weldings is not supposed to be below 550 pounds per weld. Tests performed on a three-piece sample yield the following results:

Sample No.	Shear Strength
1	580 lbs.
2	560 lbs.
3	560 lbs.

The results show not only that the three welds are within the specification limit of 550 lbs., but also the *extent* to which each differs from it. Variables tests are used to determine many different types of quality characteristics, such as dimensions of machined product, hardness of heat-treated steel, percent moisture content, electrical resistance of wire, and many other items. The one thing common to all these tests is that quality is measured along a numerical scale such as inches, pounds, ohms or any other unit of measurement. Examples have been given in previous chapters.

For simplicity, the results of variables tests are often converted to "Go Not-Go" data. The three spot welds previously mentioned might have been reported merely as "satisfactory" without regard to the numerical result.

In that case the information regarding actual shear strength in pounds would not be recorded. While this simplifies the work of the inspector, it is not desirable on processes where it is important to know *how far* a product is inside or outside specifications, so that necessary changes can be made accordingly and without loss of time. Thus the above mentioned tests of shear strength, if properly recorded by the actual pounds, will indicate any tendency for successive samples to break at loads which are close to the allowable minimum of 550 pounds. Thus, adjustments may be made in the manufacturing process before any defective material testing below this value makes its appearance.

COMPRESSED LIMIT GAGES

An innovation in technical inspection (made by British quality control engineers) consists in using gages which may be designated as "compressed limit gages" or merely as "compression gages." This method was reported by D. J. Desmond and published by the Ministry of Production in 1944. These "compressed limit gages" provide a compromise between the advantages and disadvantages of variables and "Go Not-Go" testing, and their application involves a method half-way between control charting and sampling plans. The use of compressed limit gages is best illustrated by an example:

Let us assume that a certain metal part is required to be machined to dimensions of 3″ ± .003″. Measurements of systematically selected samples, for a period of ten days, have shown that the value of the Process Variability is 0.001 inch. This means that if we were to construct a control chart, the upper control limit would be 3.002″, (3.003″ minus 0.001″) and the lower control limit would be 2.998″, (2.997″ plus .001″) ; however we do not prepare a control chart. Instead, we construct a "Go Not-Go" type gage, but with limits of 3.002 and 2.998 inches. In other words, the limits of the gage have been reduced or *"compressed"* to the width of control limits. Use of the compressed limit gage, as we shall see, makes variables determination unnecessary.

Now, we cannot go ahead and simply use a compressed limit gage instead of a regular "Go Not-Go" gage, since an allowance must be made for the fact that the limits of the compressed limit gage are narrower than the specification limits set by the engineer. An article "rejected" by the compressed limit gage with its reduced limits might still conform to the regular specification limits. However, it has been determined statistically that if 10 percent or more of the articles in a lot fail to conform to the reduced limits, then at least a small portion of them will also fail to conform to the *regular* specification limits.

All that remains to be done, therefore, is to use a sampling plan in combination with the compressed limit gage. This sampling plan should be so calculated that if a rejection occurs it is strong evidence that the process is "out of control," producing or about to produce defectives, and in need of checking and correcting. The sequential type of sampling plan recommended for use with compression gages is shown below:

Sample Size	Acceptance Number	Rejection Number
6	1	3
12	3	4

Examination of this sampling plan shows immediately that it requires considerably less inspection than the conventional sampling plans used with ordinary "Go Not-Go" testing. This is the exact purpose of a compressed limit gage. It achieves this saving in inspection because it has limits which have been reduced or "compressed" in accordance with the individual variability of a particular process.

STEPS IN COMPRESSED LIMIT GAGING

For convenience of use, the steps in compressed limit gaging are as follows:

Step 1: Determine the value of the Process Variability, as explained in Chapter 4.

Step 2: Deduct the computed value of the Process Variability from the upper specification limit and add the Process Variability to the lower specification limit. This gives the "Go" and "Not Go" dimensions for the compressed limit gage.

Step 3: Check the product with the compressed limit gage.

Step 4: Use the sampling plan below to accept or reject lots:

Sample Size	Acceptance Number	Rejection Number
6	1	3
12	3	4

Example: In the following a practical example is given of the steps involved in compressed limit gaging. The particular item selected is a machined part specified to be manufactured to dimensions of $3'' \pm 0.003$.

1. From a series of samples, the Process Variability has been computed to be 0.001 inch.

2. The upper specification limit is 3.003 inches, the lower specification limit is 2.997 inches.

$$3.003'' - .001'' = \underline{3.002''}$$

$$2.997'' + .001'' = \underline{2.998''}$$

The underlined values represent the "Go" and "Not Go" limits for the compressed limit gage.

3. The product is checked with the compressed limit gage.

4. Each lot is accepted or rejected on the basis of the sampling plan previously given under Step 4.

LIMITATIONS OF COMPRESSED LIMIT GAGING

Compressed limit gages have not yet become as popular as their theoretical advantages seemed to promise. The reason for the slow adoption of this innovation is a practical one: The limits of a compressed limit gage must be changed whenever it is found that the Process Variability has undergone a change. Such revisions of gages often involve costly tool room work.

The place of compressed limit gaging in mass production, therefore, is mainly in the control of processes which are relatively stable. An examination of inspection records accumulated over a period of several weeks will readily reveal whether or not compressed limit gages are applicable in a particular instance.

9

Use of Inspection Data in Establishing Specifications

Behind the daily routine of production and inspection stand the developments, plans and specifications for the product. Established by the designer or design engineer, they are the initial factors that decide the usefulness, economy and quality of the final merchandise. One of the functions of the inspection department is to determine whether or not the product being manufactured conforms to the specifications and tolerances. The inspection records and data obtained in this activity often provide valuable information to the engineering department in establishing and revising specifications.

COMPLEXITY OF SPECIFICATIONS

From the design of a product to the ultimate consumer there stretches a chain of requirements such as usefulness, economy and quality which form the basis for what are known technically as specifications. The user of a razor blade, for example, asks that it give him good shaves at low cost. To meet this requirement, the designer must establish specifications for dimensions, thickness, central location of perforations, temper, sharpness and appearance. These, in turn, set the pattern for the manufacturing operations of blanking, perforating, heat-treating, grinding, polishing and finishing. There must also be specifications for the quality of the steel, such as micro-structure and composition, which constitute a set of standards to be maintained by the steel mill. Specifications are the specific requirements established to maintain quality standards.

EFFECT OF PRODUCTION VARIABLES ON TOLERANCES

Realistic tolerances which are neither too close nor too wide are often difficult to set. The engineer who designs a new product and establishes specifications and tolerances for it often has no way of predicting with accuracy the effect of the many variables of production on the uniformity of the article. Even if a particular new item is produced on known equipment, there may be differences in the material, the tools and dies, the shape and dimensions or the requirements for closeness of fits and clearances. As a result, it often becomes necessary to change tolerances, and sometimes even the entire design, after an item has been in production for some time and experience with it has been gathered.

Tolerances may be either too small or too large. The costliness of such excesses in either direction is obvious. If tolerances are set too large, the product will be unsatisfactory. If tolerances are too small, the plant will incur the high cost of maintaining precision greater than really needed to make a good article. Machines and equipment may have to be stopped too frequently for re-aligning and re-adjustment and product is rejected needlessly. The information obtained by systematic inspection can often be of invaluable aid in attaining proper tolerances. How to achieve this objective will now be discussed.

WHEN TOLERANCES ARE TOO LARGE

The fact that tolerances are set too large may be established by inspection or possibly by the functioning of the completed product. Let us assume that component parts have been carefully checked after each machining operation and practically no defective product has been passed. Yet when the parts are to be assembled some of them do not fit together properly. Matching, re-working and discarding of parts becomes necessary. If the pieces are found to measure within the tolerances, then the obvious conclusion is that the tolerances are too large.

TOLERANCES FOR NON-PRECISION PRODUCTS

The importance of tolerances is often not realized where a non-precision product is manufactured. *For example,* in an air-vise assembly of a spring steel blank with a plastic handle the only specifications maintained were those for the dimensions of the pre-drilled hole and the small metal tang that was to be forced into it. Despite careful setting of the air-vise and selection of only skilled operators, a high proportion of defective assemblies—loose, cracked and bent handles—occurred. Tolerances were reduced and still no improvement resulted. Carelessness, improper electronic preheating of the handles and excessive polymerization of the plastic were blamed, until finally the chief source of defective work was discovered—varying length of the handle. Little attention had been paid to the length of the handle, since it seemed unimportant in practical use whether a tool had a handle of 4 inches or 4 1/8 inches. But it did make a difference in the way the handle fitted into the vise. If the fixture was adjusted for 4 inches, but the handle happened to measure 4 1/8 inches in length, the metal blank would be pushed just 1/8 inch deeper into the plastic than permissible and thus crack the handle. Conversely, a shorter handle would give a loose assembly. The problem was solved by establishing specifications of 4" ± 1/32" for the handle length and performing careful process inspection on the handle-shaping operation. Any future defective assemblies could be definitely traced to improper setting of the fixture, insufficient or excessive pre-heating of the handle prior to assembly, or carelessness.

WHEN TOLERANCES ARE TOO SMALL

Tolerances which are smaller than necessary may be as costly as those which are too large. They occur frequently because of the design engineer's understandable fear of "sticking his neck out." If he sets too large a tolerance, it will ultimately show up in parts which do not assemble readily with proper fits and clearances, electrical character-istics which do not fulfill requirements, or in some other way. On the other hand, small tolerances may present practical production problems and greatly increase the cost of manufacture, but they will not show up as glaring mistakes in the form of defective product.

It is not surprising, therefore, that tolerances on blueprints tend to be very conservative whereas the quantity-minded production people tend toward more liberal tolerances and the quality-minded inspector is caught in-between these opposing views. The confusion resulting from unrealistic tolerances need not be elaborated.

Inspection data can be used to advantage in a shop seriously concerned with the setting and maintaining of realistic specifications and tolerances which can be met under mass manufacturing conditions and will give a satisfactory end product.

PROCESS VARIABILITY AND TOLERANCE

Whether or not a process can normally turn out product which substantially meets the specifications depends upon the *tolerance range* and the *process variability*. A simple test can be used to tell whether or not a given process, equipment, or operation is capable of producing the required product. This test involves the following steps:

Step 1: Determine the Process Variability, as indicated in Chapter 4. (This value should be computed from samples of size 3, 4 or 5 only, the ones most commonly used. To use other sample sizes will introduce needless mathematical complications.)

Step 2: Multiply the Process Variability by 3. This will give the *process spread*.

Step 3: If the process spread is equal to or smaller than the tolerance range, it means that the process is capable of producing to the required tolerance. If the process spread is greater than the tolerance spread, then defective product is to be expected.

Example: An example will illustrate the practical use of this test:

1. From a series of four-piece samples, the Process Variability has been computed to be 0.0018″ for a machining operation on carbon steel parts.

2. 0.0018 inch multiplied by 3 equals .0054 inch. This is the *process spread*.

3. The tolerance is ± .003 inch. Therefore, the *tolerance range* is 0.006 inch. This tolerance range is slightly larger than the process spread of 0.0054 inch; therefore, the process is normally accurate enough to produce satisfactory product. It should be noted, however, that there is only a small difference between the two figures, which means that production needs to be controlled closely if defective product is to be avoided.

Determinations such as the one above are valid only for the particular equipment and product involved. A tool cutting nickel silver is generally under less strain than a tool cutting stainless steel, and one piece of equipment may have better bearings or truer beds than another. These and other variations all cause differences in accuracy and precision. In addition, variations in raw material, alertness, skill, and many other factors which "come and go" from hour to hour and day to day often combine to make exact statements about a process invalid. Despite these limitations, data regarding the process spread or accuracy of equipment have been used to great advantage by the production scheduling departments of many plants in *routing product over the most suitable lines and equipment.*

FREQUENCY DISTRIBUTIONS

Another method of determining the capabilities of a process and finding its true nature is the frequency distribution. Frequency distributions are somewhat wearisome to construct, but their information may be of paramount importance in setting tolerances realistically. An example of a frequency distribution is given in Fig. 12, which shows the result of measuring the free length of compression springs in a lot consisting of 100 pieces. Each spring is measured and the result plotted as shown in that figure.

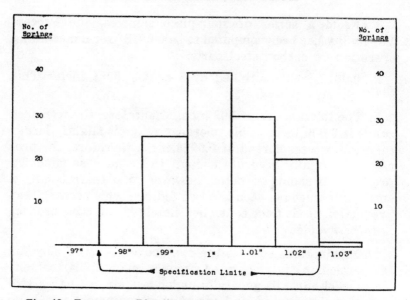

Fig. 12. Frequency Distribution Diagram Showing that Bulk of Spring Production, in This Case, is within the Specified Minimum and Maximum Limits for Length.

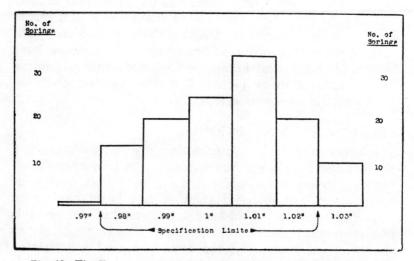

Fig. 13. The Frequency Distribution Represented by This Diagram Shows an Excessive Number of Springs Outside of the Specified Limits.

It shows the bulk of the product to be within the tolerances. Only a small and insignificant percentage falls outside. Fig. 13, on the other hand, shows a frequency distribution indicating that the production process has failed to turn out articles which substantially meet the tolerances. It is convincing proof that an investigation of the process, method of manufacture or tolerances is needed. The subject of frequency distribution will be dealt with later in Chapter 13 on Mathematical Theory of Control Charts.

CORRECTION OF TOLERANCES

When it is known that a process is not capable of normally producing pieces within the required tolerance, but that a certain percentage of non-conforming or defective articles is to be expected, several courses of action may be indicated:

1. Review the design tolerances. Perhaps they are too small and can be increased without harming the quality of the product.

2. Make engineering improvements on the process. These might require new equipment.

3. Screen each lot.

4. Consider the defectives "allowable."

The first two steps are primarily an engineering responsibility. Whether to screen lots or permit an Allowable Percent Defective is a management decision, the details of which have been presented previously.

10

Management Aspects of Quality Control

The development of modern and more effective methods of inspection has brought into the limelight the problem of fitting quality control activities into the organization in a manner that will do the most good. Modern quality control has provided production management with a new scientific tool that has shown itself capable of indicating impending trouble even before defective product makes its appearance. To make most effective use of this tool, three different types of organizational approach have been used. Each of them has its distinct advantages and disadvantages, making one or the other preferable for a particular type of manufacturing plant.

The three most commonly used organizational patterns for quality control are presented in diagram form in Fig. 14. They are based upon the fundamental fact that quality of product depends upon the coordinated activities of the production, engineering and inspection departments.

The charts furnished and the ideas presented in the following are based to a large extent upon the observations and experiences in analyzing quality control organizations by Lt. Col. A. E. Dennis, Chief of the Inspection Branch of the Philadelphia Quartermaster Depot, as presented in a paper of his on "Management's Part in Organizing and Implementing a Quality Control Program," May 2, 1945, at Alabama Polytechnic Institute.

The three types of approach, their advantages and disadvantages, are outlined in the following:

ADVISORY ORGANIZATION

Under this type of organization (see diagram at left, Fig. 14) inspectors, inspection supervisors and other inspection specialists are established as "process advisors" to production and engineering. They exercise no authority.

Advantages

1. No great changes are required. Possibility of disagreements between inspection and production is minimized.

2. If management is progressive, quality control advisors will be able to obtain cooperation in establishing quality control, particularly if it can be shown how it reduces costs.

Disadvantages

1. Lack of authority. Production executives can heed or ignore good advice, and "top" management may not be informed about the success of quality control in the plant.

2. If plant operation follows "traditional methods," human inertia will prove a stumbling block to good results.

3. Quality control advisor has no definite responsibility; therefore he lacks incentive to produce results.

DEPARTMENTALIZED ORGANIZATION

Under this type of organization, definite duties and authorities are established in the form of an inspection and quality control department. (See central diagram, Fig. 14, for details of responsibilities.)

Advantages

Quality control chief has definite responsibility; therefore he has an incentive to produce results accordingly.

Disadvantages

Quality control chief often tends to build up his prestige at the expense of production and engineering departments. May create negative reaction to the effect that quality is no concern of production and engineering executives, and

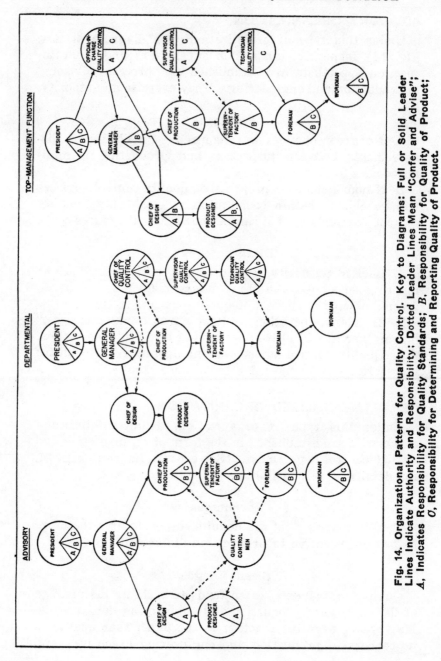

Fig. 14. Organizational Patterns for Quality Control. Key to Diagrams: Full or Solid Leader Lines Indicate Authority and Responsibility; Dotted Leader Lines Mean "Confer and Advise"; *A*, Indicates Responsibility for Quality Standards; *B*, Responsibility for Quality of Product; *O*, Responsibility for Determining and Reporting Quality of Product.

that it is entirely the responsibility of the quality control department.

2. Quality control chief cannot direct that corrective action be taken.

3. Because quality cannot be *inspected* into a product but must be designed and built into it, departmentalized, quality control is likely to be reduced to the status of a "traffic cop" separating good production from bad. Thus the "quality control" department may become merely a department for screening good product from bad.

TOP MANAGEMENT FUNCTION

Making quality control a functional part of top management means placing the quality control chief (an officer of the company, if desired) in a position similar to that of controller. Specific duties may be assigned as shown by diagram at right, Fig. 14.

Advantages

1. Quality control chief can place responsibility for quality where it belongs, direct that corrective action be taken where necessary and establish company policy as regards quality.

2. If functions have been carefully defined, this gives the quality control personnel positive duties and responsibilities as well as a chance for adequate reward.

3. Authority is established to accumulate facts and figures and to direct what is to be done about them.

Disadvantages

1. Functional organization may produce resentment on the part of those who believe that their authority is impaired.

2. Danger of improper distinction of duties.

A conclusion regarding the over-all merit of any one of the methods just outlined cannot be stated, since much depends upon the individuality of a particular business organization and the type of manufacturing. In chemical manufacturing, for example, where considerable attention is paid to tests and test results, the advisory type of organization may be the best. This type, however, usually would be ineffective in many types of precision metal work. Here the departmental organization may be preferable in small plants and functional organization in large plants. The personal element involved, such as the attitude of management, the extent to which management is ready to promote quality control, and the personality of the quality control chief play a decisive role in the choice of a successful system.

OBTAINING COOPERATION AND COMPLIANCE

To obtain effective quality control, it is of paramount importance to obtain the cooperation of production people and to induce them to comply readily with whatever necessary corrections are brought out through inspection. This in turn requires not only proper organization and management, but fair and impartial inspection, as well as an understanding of the aims of inspection by production personnel.

In order to present clearly the important principles of quality control and its effective use, simple illustrations of principles will be a helpful means of supplementing an education and training program throughout the plant. They may be incorporated in standard practice manuals or be exhibited as posters in connection with whatever methods are in use at the particular plant involved.

11

A Typical Case History

We shall now present a case history of a quality control installation in a metal working plant. The example chosen has been taken from the manufacture of cutlery and flatware, since it represents relatively simple operations and yet includes such universal processes as blanking, perforating, forming and other press-work; grinding and drilling; forging; casting; polishing, plating and finishing. An attempt has been made to bring out principles and basic ideas involved, from which the inspection supervisor can obtain the information needed for his own product.

REPORTS TO TOP MANAGEMENT

The case history is presented in the form of two reports to top management: The first is a memorandum recommending installation of modern quality control techniques, outlining the proposed steps, and asking for the necessary authorization to go ahead with the plan. The second is a report of the result achieved. While the case history is based on actual experience, the data have been changed to conceal confidential information. This should not affect their usefulness for purposes of illustration.

Since much of the success of quality control depends upon recognition of the inspector's work by top management, the inspection supervisor may find it desirable to make similar reports of his own work. The two reports follow:

Report to Mr. S. Smith, Works Manager
on
RECOMMENDATIONS FOR ESTABLISHMENT OF
MODERN QUALITY CONTROL IN THE PLANT.

This report contains recommendations for
the introduction of certain approved quality

control techniques in the Greenville plant of
ABC Company. These methods have been finding
increasing adoption throughout industry, as
a means of controlling economically and
efficiently the quality of mass production.

In general, the techniques proposed for
adoption are adapted from those recommended
officially as the most practical and efficient
by the American Society for Testing Materials,
the American Standards Associations, and by
many prominent industrial organizations.
These techniques are known as "sampling-for-
quality-control" and "statistical quality
control." The word 'statistical' here refers
to the use of mathematical probability in
analyzing inspection data and the engineering
use of the data in controlling production.

If the general methods proposed in the
following meet with approval, authorization
is desired for carrying them into effect.
These will be outlined somewhat in detail
because of their economic importance in
our plant.

The Present System:

In the light of modern concepts and recent
investigations, it may be said that while our
inspection system is technically correct, it
has certain weaknesses in methods. These are:

1. Undue reliance is placed upon our few
roving process inspectors to control production.
Since they cannot be in all places at one time,
process inspection is far from adequate and
should not be relied upon as a primary means
of quality control.

2. Undue reliance is placed upon 100 percent
screening inspection, by bench inspectors, to
sort out defective product. Spot checks made
have shown that from 2 to 3 percent of
defectives have remained in lots after they
had been screened. This observation merely
bears out studies made in many industrial plants
which showed that due to fatigue and monotony
in screening inspection, as much as 15 percent
of all bad product may be overlooked. Thus, if

a lot should happen to contain 7 percent defectives, about 1 percent defectives may still
remain in it after screening has been performed.

The Solution of Present Difficulties:

   The existing quality problem will not be
solved by hiring more roving process inspectors
or by doing more bench inspecting. Neither
will there be permanent results by instructing
inspectors to be more watchful, since the
majority of them are known to be doing as well
as can be expected normally. Instead, it is
recommended that an entirely different system
of inspection be adopted: sampling-for-quality-
control. This technique aims to utilize inspection data as much as possible in anticipating
and preventing the production of defectives.

How Sampling-For-Quality-Control Works:

   The application of sampling-for-quality-
control in this plant is best illustrated by
showing how it would work in one department,
as, for example, the Drop-Hammer Department:

   Step 1:   One inspector draws periodically a
             random-representative sample from
             the blanks produced on each drop-
             hammer.

   Step 2:   When the inspector has drawn the
             required number of sample pieces,
             he takes them to his bench and gives
             them a very careful examination.
             If necessary, he will compare a
             questionable piece against standard
             samples showing borderline quality
             margins for surface imperfections,
             etc., or check it against his
             "Standard Inspection List" showing
             what are classed as "major" and
             "minor" defects.

   Step 3:   After the inspector has examined
             every piece in his sample, he counts
             the number of defectives found (if
             any) and compares them against a
             sampling table worked out for him

by the Quality Control Department.
This table tells him when to accept
lots and when to reject them for poor
quality, on the basis of previously
established quality standards.

Step 4:   If the total number of defective
pieces found by the inspector is
equal to or smaller than the
permissible number, given in his
sampling table, the inspector knows
that in all probability the lot from
which the sample was drawn contains
such a small percentage of defectives
(if any) that it is acceptable;
consequently, the lot is passed to
the next stage of production.
If the total number of defective
pieces found exceeds the permissible
number, it is strong evidence that
the lot contains an excessive
percentage of defectives; therefore,
the inspector rejects the lot,
notifying the foreman that corrective
action on the process must be taken
immediately to stop defective
production. The bad lot itself is
"detailed" to screen out all defectives by 100 percent inspection.

Preventing Production of Defectives

The important difference between screening
and sampling-for-quality-control is now
apparent. Screening serves merely to separate
defectives from good product. Sampling-for-
quality-control is designed primarily to obtain
inspection data for use either in preventing
defective production, or in stopping it where
it occurs and as quickly as possible. This is
the principal problem in our plant.

Basis of Sampling Tables

Management must allow for the fact that in
mass production of blanks a certain small
percentage of defective output is unavoidable.

This percentage, the Allowable Percent Defective, is determined from the following factors:

1. The cost of further processing defective pieces, which will finally be scrapped.

2. The quality that may reasonably be expected under mass production conditions.

3. The normal effect of the many variables of production on the uniformity of the process.

The sampling tables furnished to the inspector by the Quality Control Department take into account the Allowable Percent Defective as well as the ever-present sampling risks:

1. Risk of accepting a bad lot as "good."

2. Risk of rejecting a good lot as "bad."

These risks can be reduced to a minimum by furnishing the inspector with sampling tables that have been determined by mathematical probability calculations supported by practical judgment.

Quality Improvement:

It was pointed out that sampling-for-quality-control is designed to detect and stop defective output when and where it occurs; moreover, data accumulated over a period of time will indicate where additional training of operators is needed, where special maintenance of equipment is required and where basic changes in methods of operation, equipment or design may be desirable.

Primary Responsibility for Quality

The purpose of the modernized inspection department will be to help the production floor more effectively in turning out an acceptable product. It does not replace the primary responsibility for quality, which rests with the foremen and workmen, as it has in the past.

Organization for Quality Control

In order to obtain effective quality control, it is necessary to establish a managerial relationship which will assure prompt action on the process whenever inspection data indicate lack of control. A suggested organization for this purpose is shown in Exhibit 1 (Diagram at right of Fig. 14). An important feature of this chart is that quality control is made a function of top management and that the inspection and Quality Control Department is independent of either Production or Engineering departments. This separation is highly important because quality is the result of efforts by both Engineering and Production departments and quality control should be free to establish the facts as they are, uninfluenced by either engineering or production considerations.

H. Brown
Chief Inspector.

Report to Mr. S. Smith, Works Manager
on
REVIEW OF THE FIRST TWO MONTHS' RESULTS
OF OUR MODERNIZED QUALITY CONTROL PROGRAM

Balance Between Quality and Quantity

There are many problems that have arisen in our program of installing and maintaining an up-to-date quality control system, but they all reduce ultimately to one major problem, that is, how to maintain a standard level of quality and at the same time obtain the quantity of production required. All other problems are merely contributing factors to this major one.

It became apparent soon after we installed the Quality Control Program, that the attainment and maintenance of quality of production would be complicated by a multitude of factors arising from the need for quantity production. The Inspection Department found that it would

have to travel a middle road between quality
and quantity: guarding against excessive
relaxation of quality standards to assure
volume of production, while at the same time
isolating unsatisfactory operations, operators
or machinery which could be corrected without
appreciable loss in production.

This dilemma was aggravated by the fact
that not enough experienced inspectors have
been available to provide adequate supervision
of operations plus skilled examination of
product. For although inspection has always
consumed a great number of man-hours at ABC Co.
(about 500 hours per week, as shown by a
survey), the majority of qualified inspectors
were found to be part-time production workers
(die-setters, assistant foremen, piece-rate
men) who were little interested in a full-time
inspection job because of the relatively lower
compensation offered by the Inspection
Department. Personnel doing inspection 100
percent of the time were found to be experienced
in only certain types of operations (such as
examination of tinning and pointing only, or
grinding only, or plating only, etc.) and
stationed at points where inspection was merely
segregating but not corrective. For example,
inspectors were sorting out bad blanks and
die-cast bolsters from good ones before assembly
in the Assembly Department, while they should
have been working in the departments where the
defects actually occur. The extensive shifts
in inspection to the most effective locations,
involved considerable un-learning and re-
training, both in the technique of examining
individual pieces of product as well as
determining the acceptability of lots through
sampling inspection.

Throughout the program, emphasis has been
placed on installing lot-by-lot inspection and
control charts at the points in production
where they would do the most good in detecting
defective work and stopping the outflow of
unsatisfactory products. As a result, the
former high cost of 100 percent inspection of
articles prior to assembly has been eliminated.

Standardization of Inspection

Specifications for methods, quality of finish
and workmanship are given for each item by the
time-study record; hence, it was necessary that
the basis for accepting and rejecting lots
be standardized for all operations so that
every operator receives the same treatment.

STANDARD INSPECTION LIST
FOR
KNIFE BLADES FOLLOWING MIRROR FINISHING

EXAMINE	MAJOR DEFECT	MINOR DEFECT
Entire blade	Scorch marks Glaze marks Scratches	Satin Finish
	Dark Brown Burns[1]	Light Brown Burns[1]
Back	Burrs not Removed	Worn Thin
	Nicks	
Tip	Nicks	Worn Thin
Edge	Uneven Taper	
	Thick[2] Thin[2]	
	Wet Grind Marks Not Removed	

1 = Compare with standard sample.

2 = Use go-nogo gage to determine proper
    thickness.

This required standardizing and unifying the
methods, practices and controls of all phases
of inspection.

Standardization of inspection has been
approached from two points of view: inspection
of the individual blank (technical) and inspection of the lot (statistical). The technical
side of the problem is being solved by
preparation of written Standard Inspection Lists
(see accompanying example) and standardized
product nomenclatures for all items and
operations. The statistical side of the
problem is being solved by collecting and
analyzing inspection data to arrive at values
of the "Allowable Percent Defective" for each
item and the issuance of the standard sampling
plans based on these factors.

Gages and Templets

With the aid of the Engineering Department,
continued progress has been made in the
development of gages and templets to control
such important variables as contours of blanks
after drop-hammer operations, the width of
tangs before and after slush-casting, the
thickness of blades after grinding and glazing,
etc. The use of gages eliminates difficult and
time-consuming measurements.

Sampling Plans

Our type of manufacturing is at such high
rate of speed and the value of the individual
article produced so small, relatively, that
it does not warrant screening except in the
Packing Department, where 100 percent examination
is done to prevent shipment of defective
merchandise as much as possible. It is
necessary, however, to determine the quality
of each lot in process after certain operations.
After striking of blanks, for example, lot-by-lot
sampling inspection is performed to isolate
any hammers on which excessive scrap is being
produced, as, for example, by wearing or shift-
ing of dies or careless operation. This makes
it possible to take immediate corrective action;

but that is not the only function of quality
control sampling. In the Finishing Department,
for example, it must be ascertained that blanks
are properly polished before plating. At the
same time it would not be economical to examine
every tote box of 500 pieces, for many of them
will contain only a few defective (poorly
polished) pieces. Here again application of
sampling plans solves the problem: if the
sample indicates that the lot (tote box of 500)
contains only a very small permissible number
of defectives, the lot is permitted to move on
to plating without further inspection. However,
if the sample indicates that the lot probably
contains more defectives than allowable, then
the entire lot is detailed to 100 percent
screening inspection. Thus, the defectives are
sorted out, to be done over by the person
responsible for them, before they are plated.
Preventive action is necessary to insure a
minimum amount of defectives after plating,
since it is costly to correct them.

Quality Improvement

Observations in many departments already show
gratifying results as regards quality of
product. This is borne out by the attached
graphs (Figs. 15, 16 and 17), representing
departments where quality control inspection
methods have been in effect for some time.

Fig. 15 shows the decrease in scrap output
following installation of lot-by-lot inspection
in Drop Hammer Department. Part of this decrease
is due to psychological causes: the knowledge
that his work is being systematically inspected
makes the operator more quality minded—
previously nobody had seemed to care much.
More important, however, is the fact that
lot-by-lot inspection data were analyzed to
single out worn dies, poor set-ups and,
occasionally, carelessness.

A reduction of scrap produced in this department, from a yearly average of 2.5 percent to
approximately 1 percent, results in an average
weekly saving of raw materials alone amounting

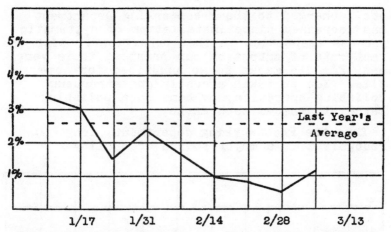

Fig. 15. Graph Showing Weekly Percentage of Decrease in Scrap
Output from Drop Hammers, Following Installation of Lot-by-Lot
Inspection. Data Compiled from Cost Department Records.

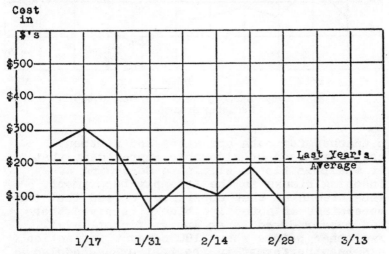

Fig. 16. Graph Showing Reduction in Cost of Re-work Operations
in Press Department. Data Compiled from Payroll Analysis.

to $116.50. A breakdown of this figure for
carbon steel, stainless steel, nickel-silver and
brass may be obtained from the Cost Department.

Fig. 16 shows how the reduction in cost of
rework operations due to die marks, flashes,

etc., charged to the Pressworking Department
has decreased since installation of systematic
process inspection in that Department. With the
fast rate of output on our presses, it is very
easy for die marks to go unnoticed for some
time. Yet it takes a costly and strenuous
polishing operation, by hand on a polishing
lathe, to remove such marks.

Thus the Pressworking department, long
recognized as a major source of quality

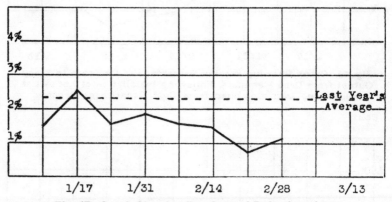

Fig. 17. Graph Showing Per Cent of Defectives from
Polishing Department.

headaches for both operators and foremen,
has shown such considerable improvement that
it was possible to eliminate screening of
incoming blanks in the Assembly Department.
The foreman of that department agreed that the
percentage of defective blanks received there
had been reduced to an insignificant level.
Two other points where 100 percent inspection
has been performed in the past are scheduled
to be replaced by lot-by-lot sampling also.

Striking improvements in quality were also
achieved in the Polishing (Fig. 17) and
Finishing Departments.

Materials Inspection

A considerable amount of inspection has
always been performed on incoming materials;

such as steel coils and strips, plastic handles, grommets, bars, etc. The inspector keeps simple records of his findings, which are later combined into "quality histories" for each major supplier. These quality histories (see Fig. 18 for an example) will be used by the Purchasing Department as a guide to the placement of future orders with the most reliable sources of raw material. In a sense, therefore, quality control begins in the steel mill.

Limiting Factors

Our quality control program depends on the successful use of technical inspection equipment, Standard Inspection Lists, and sampling plans. The human element is the limiting factors in all cases.

Proper use of equipment, inspection lists and sampling plans is being emphasized through training programs and rechecking of actual work accomplished. However, there is still a long road to travel, especially as regards inspection of product that may be of so-called "borderline" quality.

Cost Savings

While the forthcoming quarterly operating statement prepared by the Accounting Department reflects tangible savings due to a reduction of scrap and rework, the more significant long range gains arising from our quality control program cannot be stated in figures as yet.

The most important factor here probably is the increased goodwill among foremen and workmen created through orderly and systematic inspection in which decisions to reject lots or stop faulty operations and set-ups are not based on "arbitrary" judgment, but on the impartial indications provided by sampling plans and control charts. Mistakes in rejections still occur, but they are few and far apart. In many instances, the improved uniformity of product moving from one operation to the next has

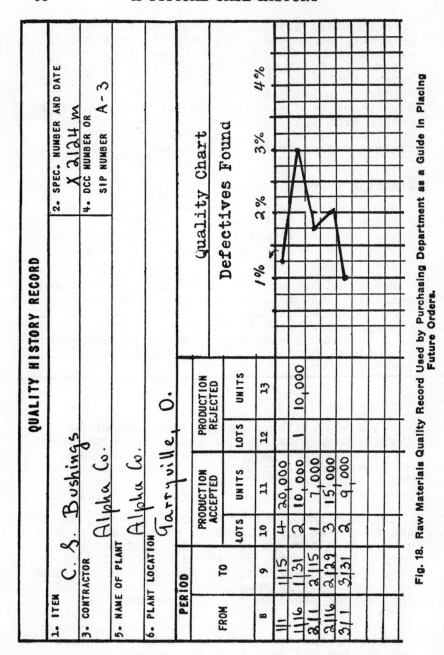

Fig. 18. Raw Materials Quality Record Used by Purchasing Department as a Guide In Placing Future Orders.

permitted a reduction of down-time and speeding up of output, thereby fattening piece-workers' pay envelopes.

Examination of outgoing products has revealed striking gains in the appearance of our regular merchandise—clearer patterns, truer contours and a generally higher quality of finish. These are improvements which cannot be presented in the form of figures, but they have been recognized by the Sales Department. In the long run, this improved quality will make our merchandise more competitive by appealing to the comparison shopper and by increasing the acceptance of our product by our dealers who readily detect changes in quality.

Within the next few months, it is contemplated to introduce additional refinements of methods. In particular, it is planned to set up quality control charts on our drilling and shaping equipment and to install additional sampling plans where needed.

Continuing progress is made towards close cooperation with the Purchasing Department in the elimination of unsatisfactory sources of supply of raw materials and to present essential inspection data to the Engineering Department, which may be useful in initiating changes in machinery or product design or serve as a basis for setting and reviewing tolerance or other specifications.

H. Brown, Chief Inspector
K. Clark, Assistant

While this case history relates to one plant, it will not be difficult to draw parallel conclusions regarding the proper approach to problems arising in other types of manufacturing plants. The universal applicability of modern scientific quality control methods has been indicated throughout this book by the variety of manufacturing processes and operations used to illustrate its practical application.

12

Statistical Basis of Modern Quality Control

A reading of this Chapter is not essential for the practical application of scientific quality control, but many progressive inspectors who have studied the practical part of this book will not be satisfied with ready-made sampling plans and control charts and will want to know how and where the science of statistics and mathematical probability enters into such plans and charts. This chapter is for such inspectors.

SIMPLE EXAMPLE OF MATHEMATICAL PROBABILITY

To understand how the law of probability works in sampling inspection, we will take a simple example of probability mathematics. Let us assume that 100 bowls each contain 96 white (or good) marbles and 4 black (or bad) marbles. Each bowl of marbles is considered as being a lot. Now we want to find out how it will work out if we use the following sampling plan on each lot:

Sample Size	Acceptance Number	Rejection Number
5	0	1

How many lots will be accepted and how many will be rejected under this sampling plan? After you have gone through the trouble of sampling all 100 bowls, the chances are that finally 82 lots will be accepted and 18 lots rejected. This may seem odd, since the rejected 18 lots are of exactly the same quality as the accepted ones.

The conclusion may be that the sampling plan is not satisfactory and that there should be one which gives better results. So you may vary the acceptance and rejection numbers, or the sample size, and start sampling again. But soon you will be tired of sampling marbles and will want an easier solution of the problem.

CALLING IN THE MATHEMATICIAN

Suppose you call in a mathematician and confront him with the problem. This man does not bother at all with samples. Instead he presents the following analysis of the problem:

Since each bowl contains 4 black marbles and 96 white marbles, it is obvious that if you take just *one* marble at random from any bowl, the odds are 96 to 100 that this marble will be a white one. Instead of saying that the odds are 96 to 100, you can also say that the chances are 96 percent or 0.96. Now if you draw *two* marbles from any bowl, the chances that *both* will be white are 0.96 × 0.96, which is equal to 0.92 approximately. This means that the odds are 92 to 100 that the two marbles will both be white ones.

The sampling plan calls for a sample of *five* marbles. What are the chances of drawing only white ones in this sample? They are 0.96 × 0.96 × 0.96 × 0.96 × 0.96, which is equal to 0.815 or approximately 82 percent. (An exact method would be to multiply $\dfrac{96}{100} \times \dfrac{95}{99} \times \dfrac{94}{98} \times \dfrac{93}{97} \times \dfrac{92}{96}$, which gives you 0.812 or approximately 81 percent.)

Compare the figure (0.82) with the one found in the experiment of sampling all 100 bowls, and you will see that in all probability they will both be the same. The mathematician's figure, however, is arrived at by calculation and without doing any actual sampling at all.

ANOTHER SAMPLING PLAN

"All right," you say, "but how about this: According to the sampling plan, I would have rejected 18 lots which were just as good as the accepted ones; therefore the sampling plan is unsatisfactory. Can you use probability mathematics to figure out a better sampling plan for me? I want one that gives me at least 98 percent acceptances."

"Certainly," replies the mathematician. He takes his pencil and after some figuring gives you the following plan:

Sample Size	Acceptance Number	Rejection Number
5	1	2

TRANSLATION INTO PRACTICE

"Very good," you say. "Now let us go on to some problem which is more like the ones with which I have to cope in practice. Suppose we have a number of bowls each containing 500 marbles, but this time we do not know how many marbles are black and how many marbles are white. The only thing known is that the lot is to be rejected if it contains more than 4 percent black marbles. Is 100 percent inspection necessary in this case or is there a simpler method by way of mathematics?"

"There is," the mathematician tells you. "The laws of probability can provide you with a sampling plan which tells you with *reasonable* accuracy whether a lot is acceptable or not. This is such a plan:

Sample Size	Acceptance Number	Rejection Number
50	3	4

You ask: "What do you mean by 'reasonable accuracy'?"

"Obviously," the mathematician answers, "sampling is not so foolproof a way for judging the quality of a lot as 100 percent inspection. In exchange for the advantage of inspecting only 50 of the 500 marbles, you have to take into the bargain a risk of up to 15 percent that you will reject a satisfactory lot. A satisfactory lot is, of course, a lot containing up to the allowable percent of defectives — 4 percent in our example."

"This risk," you reply, "appears too high for practical purposes. I want a sampling plan in which the odds of rejecting a satisfactory lot are only 10 percent.

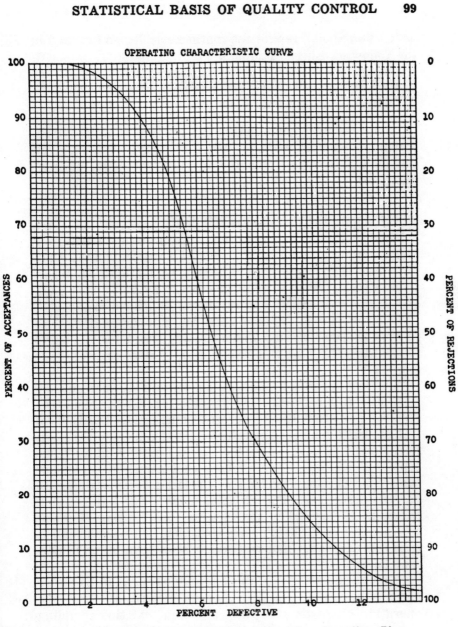

Fig. 19. Operating Characteristic Curve of a Sampling Plan,
Showing Per Cent of Acceptances and Rejections.

"As you wish," replies the mathematician, and gives you the following Single Sampling Plan.

Sample Size	Acceptance Number	Rejection Number
100	6	7

"But," he adds, "you see that larger samples are required, which means more work for added security. And thus you can have a sampling plan for any desired degree of sampling risk.

OPERATING CHARACTERISTIC CURVES

Now pose your last question: "I am going to use your last sampling plan in the shop. There I am confronted daily with lots each containing different percentages of defectives, varying from 0 to 10 or more. By using this plan, how many acceptances and rejections do I have to expect?"

"That of course depends upon the number of defectives in each lot you inspect. The operating characteristic curve of the sampling plan will give you the desired answer. (See Fig. 19.)

"Suppose your lot happens to contain 10 percent defectives. Refer to the bottom scale labeled "Percent Defective" and from the 10 percent point follow the vertical line up, until you reach the curve. On this level to the right is the point 85 percent on the vertical scale reading "Percent of Rejections." This means that about 85 percent of the time this sampling plan will reject a lot containing 10 percent defectives. On the same level to the left you find the point 15 percent on the vertical scale reading "Percent of Acceptances." This means that about 15 percent of the time this sampling plan will accept a lot containing 10 percent defectives.

"Now suppose the quality of the lot happens to be better and the lot contains only 2 percent defectives. Then the operating characteristic curve tells you that this sampling plan will accept such a lot 99 percent of the time and reject it 1 percent of the time."

There is an operating characteristic curve for every sam-

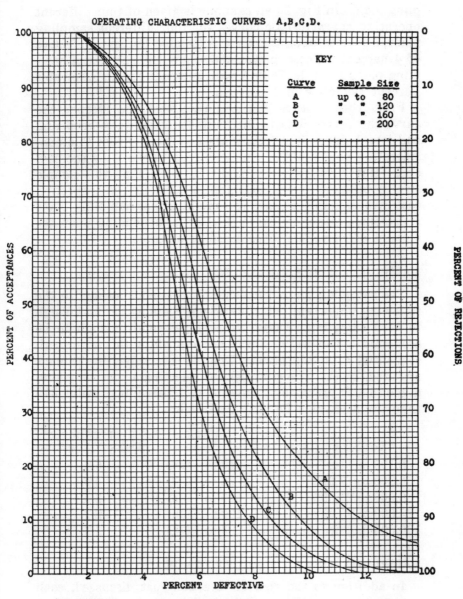

OPERATING CHARACTERISTIC CURVES A,B,C,D.

KEY

Curve	Sample Size		
A	up to		80
B	"	"	120
C	"	"	160
D	"	"	200

Fig. 20. Four Different Operating Characteristic Curves for Four Different Sampling Plans.

pling plan. In Fig. 20 an example is given of four different operating characteristic curves for four different sampling plans, all based upon the same Allowable Percent Defective of 4 percent. These curves show how the sequential sampling plans given in Table 1 will work out for an Allowable Percent Defective of 4 percent.

From these curves you will note that the steeper the curve the better it is in discriminating between good and bad lots, because it rejects more bad lots. From this consideration you would of course choose Curve D as the best one. But circumstances might be such that the sample size to be inspected is too high because of the inspection cost involved. In that case you might utilize sampling plans represented either by curve C, B or A, depending upon the amount of inspection considered practicable.

SAMPLING RISKS OF REJECTION

The sampling plans furnished in this book recognize the following important principle: Samples must be big enough to keep sampling risks down and yet small enough to be economical. The best means of accomplishing this is through sequential sampling plans. The plans supplied by Table 1 are based on the following risks of rejecting a good lot where a good lot is assumed to have ½ to 1 percentage point less than the Allowable Percent Defective:

Lot Size	Sample Size	Approximate Risk of Rejection
3,199 or less	40 to 200	5%
3,200 to 7,999	50 to 300	4%
8,000 to 21,999	100 to 500	3%
22,000 to 99,999	100 to 1,000	2%
100,000 and up	200 to 1,600	1%

SAMPLING RISKS OF ACCEPTANCE

In addition to the risk of rejection just discussed, each sampling plan entails also a "risk of acceptance." This refers to the possibility that occasionally a bad lot may be erroneously accepted, due to the "luck of draw" in sampling.

Since these risks vary depending upon what is considered to be a "bad lot," the following table has been drawn up to show for a 4 percent Allowable Defective the risk of accepting bad lots containing 5, 6, 7, 8 and 9 percent defectives respectively.

Table 7. Risk of Acceptance for 4 Per Cent Allowable Defectives

Lot Size	Sequential Sample Size	Per Cent Defectives in Bad Lot				
		5	6	7	8	9
		Percent Risk of Acceptance				
Up to 499	40 to 80	78	64	47	35	25
500 to 799	40 to 120	72	53	36	23	15
800 to 1,299	40 to 160	65	43	26	15	8
1,300 to 3,199	50 to 200	59	34	17	9	4
3,200 to 7,999	50 to 300	48	21	9	3	1
8,000 to 21,999	100 to 500	34	10	2	1	Nil
22,000 and up	100 to 1,600	10	2	Nil	Nil	Nil

The risks of acceptance appear to be large, particularly for the smaller lot sizes and one might well ask how is it possible to maintain an Allowable Percent Defective of only 4 percent if, for a lot size of 499 or less there is a risk of 3 chances out of 4 that a lot containing 5 percent defectives will be accepted, 2 chances out of 3 that a lot containing 6 percent defectives will be accepted, 1 chance out of 2 that a lot containing 7 percent defectives will be accepted, 1 chance out of 3 that a lot containing 8 percent defectives will be accepted, and 1 chance out of 4 that a lot containing 9 percent defectives will be accepted. The answer to this is that where there is no screening of rejected lots, such a quality level could not be maintained. The sequential sampling plans shown in Table 1 have been drawn up on the assumption that there will be such screening. Where this is so, the theoretically perfect lots resulting from screening will tend to balance the bad lots that slip through due to the

Table 8A. Sampling Risks of Acceptance Corresponding to Sampling Plans in Table 1.

Percent Risk of Acceptance

Lot Size	Sample Size	Allowable Percent Defective: 0.5		1.0		2.0		3.0		5.0			6.0			8.0			10.0		
		Percent Defective in Production Lot: 1.0	2.0	2.0	4.0	3.0	5.0	4.0	6.0	6.0	8.0	10.0	7.0	9.0	12.0	10.0	12.0	15.0	12.0	15.0	18.0
499 or less	40 to 80	....	....	....	....	75	40	73	42	80	52	30	81	59	26	75	68	23	80	50	26
500 to 799	40 to 120	....	....	69	28	70	30	64	25	73	40	15	78	47	15	63	48	10	68	30	10
800 to 1,299	40 to 160	....	....	62	19	63	20	55	20	70	30	10	75	38	9	60	40	8	65	22	5
1,300 to 3,199	50 to 200	60	25	55	10	50	10	45	10	60	20	4	68	30	5	50	26	4	55	17	3
3,200 to 7,999	50 to 300	50	10	40	2	45	5	30	4	50	10	1	64	20	2	38	18	2	50	10	Nil
8,000 to 21,999	100 to 500	30	2	22	Nil	40	3	20	2	35	4	Nil	55	10	Nil	25	8	1	43	6	Nil
22,000 to 99,999	100 to 1,000	10	Nil	10	Nil	10	Nil	10	Nil	20	2	Nil	35	3	Nil	....	....	....	....	....	....
100,000 and up	200 to 1,600	2	Nil	3	Nil	5	Nil	5	Nil	10	Nil	Nil	....	....	....	....	....	....	....	....	....

Notes: 1. "Nil" indicates that risk is negligible.
2. Table 1 does not provide sampling plans where .... are shown.

risks of acceptance just discussed. Thus, if the perfect lots are combined with the imperfect ones, the total percentage of bad product which is finally passed will, for the sampling plans presented in Table 1, under no circumstances exceed the Allowable Percent Defective given therein. In technical language this feature of the sampling plans is known as Average Outgoing Quality Limit (A.O.Q.L.) protection.

Where it is not possible or practical to screen rejected lots, then the best course is to set up tests or examination of the product in such a way as to yield "variables" data and then to use a control chart such as is described in Chapter 4 on Process Inspection.

Prior to making such a decision, Chapter 6 on Applying Quality Control in the Plant should be reviewed, for an evaluation of the relative merits of installing either a control chart or a sampling plan under the particular conditions of manufacturing that may be involved.

TABLES OF SAMPLING RISKS OF ACCEPTANCE

The risks of acceptance which were shown in Table 7 cover only those sampling plans in Table 1 for an Allowable Percent Defective of 4 percent. In actual practice, you may be using another sampling plan, such as for 0.5 percent Allowable Percent Defective, or 2 percent or some other percentage and it may be desired to evaluate the sampling risks of acceptance involved. For this purpose, Table 8A for Sampling Risks of Acceptance is furnished. This table is not as detailed as the special tabulation shown in Table 7, and it also omits some of the lesser used values of the Allowable Percent Defective. It is felt, however, that for practical purposes this extra detail is not needed. For any values not listed, the approximate sampling risk may still be evaluated by means of interpolation. The risks shown are accurate within plus or minus ten percent. Thus, for example, under an Allowable Percent Defective of 5 and Lot Size 1,300 to 3,199, associated with sample size 50 to 100, we find that a lot with 8 percent defectives may slip through 20 percent of the time. This value of 20 percent may actually turn out to be 18 or 22, since ten percent of 20 percent is 2, and we must allow a tolerance of plus or minus 2 for inaccuracies. These are theoretical considerations as far as the practical use of the sampling tables is concerned. They do demonstrate, however, that the problem of sampling and sampling risks is a complex one, and that statistical methods are indeed essential in setting up a sound sampling program in any plant or shop.

Although in this discussion of sampling risks, reference has been made to the sequential plans in Table 1, these risks apply equally to Table 2 for single sampling plans. As was pointed out, Table 2 was especially computed so as to entail risks identical to the ones pertaining to Table 1. The only difference between the two tables is the amount of sampling required.

Having explained the sampling risks associated with use of Table 1, Master Sampling Table, we will now examine the risks in the additional Tables that were provided in Chapters 2 and 3. Table 2, "Master Table of Single Sampling Plans" was set up to correspond to Table 1, and the sampling risks are practically identical. This was explained in Chapter 2. For Table 3, "Master Sampling Table for Continuous Items of Product" the risks of acceptance are as shown in Table 8B. The risks of rejection are 5 percent, with a "good lot" being defined as one containing the Allowable Percent Defective. Here again, Table 4, "Master Single Sampling Table for Continuous Items of Product" involves sampling risks which are practically identical to those shown for Table 3 and need not be listed separately. It will be recalled that for continuous items of product, the rule of random sampling cannot be adhered to strictly. Therefore if defects are not randomly distributed throughout such a lot, the validity of the sampling risks shown here is impaired to some extent. Usually, however, this factor does not become of practical significance if the amount of sampling is relatively large and the Allowable Percent Defective is above 1 percent. These two elements have been taken into account in preparing Tables 3 and 4. Where the distribution of defects is not approximately random or other reasons prevent use of such sampling plans, then 100 percent inspection remains as the sole alternative.

Table 8B. Sampling Risks of Acceptance Corresponding to Sampling Plans in Table 3.

Lot Size	Sample Size	Allowable Percent Defective																							
		2		3		4		5		6		8		10		12		15		17		20		25	
	Percent Defective in Production Lot	3	4	4	5	5	7	6	8	7	9	9	12	12	14	14	16	16	20	19	22	22	25	27	30
	Risk of Acceptance in Percent																								
9,999 or less	525 to 1275	70	20	73	25	85	15	85	18	85	20	88	15	72	21	76	25	75	15	87	25	80	25	85	29
10,000 to 24,999	600 to 1500	65	13	65	20	78	8	82	12	83	15	85	7	65	12	70	17	71	8	86	20	76	15	80	20
25,000 to 49,999	675 to 1800	63	10	62	15	74	5	80	8	81	12	82	5	62	9	63	12	68	5	85	15	75	13	78	18
50,000 or more	825 to 2025	60	8	59	10	70	2	75	5	79	9	79	4	60	8	61	10	62	2	84	12	71	10	73	12

13

Mathematical Theory of Control Charts

None of the material in this chapter is required for practical application of the control chart technique furnished in the preceding parts of this book. However, it does bring out the fundamental facts on the statistical theory behind such charts, in terms of elementary algebra. It should therefore be of interest to many readers, and should definitely be understood by those desirous of investigating in detail the more refined techniques presented in Part II of this book.

CAUSES AND EFFECTS OF VARIATION

Fundamental to all production is the fact that quality of any mass-manufactured product, as measured from unit to unit or from lot to lot, shows *variations*. There are many causes which account for this. For example, in the manufacture of a machined product, play in bearings, slight maladjustments, vibration, raw material imperfections, and temperature changes may combine in various ways to prevent perfect uniformity. Similar factors operate in chemical production, textile milling, or any other process. A further important element causing variation stems from the human factor which is involved to a certain degree in most types of production. These are familiar facts in inspection experience.

To study the effects of variation, let us take a machined part which has a basic dimension of 1 inch. Because of the impossibility of attaining exactly 1 inch, the engineer has to specify the degree of accuracy which he considers essential for the proper functioning of the part and which is economical to maintain under mass production conditions. Let us assume the specification reads 1 ± .003 inch. As previously explained, this means that the desired or *nominal* dimension is 1 inch, but that a part measuring somewhere between 0.997 inch and 1.003 inch is satisfactory. Thus, the machine operator has a tolerance for permissible variation.

FREQUENCY PATTERN

Now experience has shown in hundreds of thousands of instances that if production is carried on with proper care

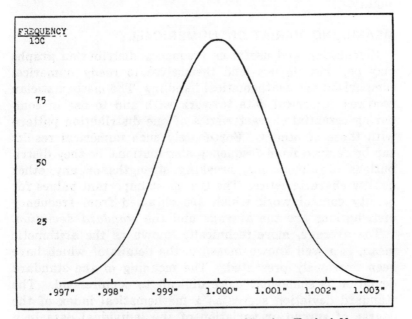

Fig. 21. Frequency Distribution Curve Showing Typical Manner in which a Machined Product may be Found to Vary within the Specification Limits.

and accuracy, the resultant lot will be distributed in a so-called "normal" pattern such as shown in Fig. 21. In this graph each work-piece is arranged according to its measured dimension and the number of times or *frequency* with which each dimension occurs is plotted. The graph is therefore called a *frequency distribution* or *frequency pattern*.

As shown in the diagram, most of the product centers

around 1 inch, falling between dimensions of 0.999 inch and 1.001 inch. A smaller portion measures between 0.998 — 0.999 inch and 1.001 — 1.002 inch, with a still smaller proportion between the extreme values of 0.998 — 0.997 inch and 1.002 — 1.003 inch. From this it is evident that the operator succeeded in producing most of the parts very close to the nominal specification of 1.000 inch. None of the product fell outside the specification limits of 0.997 inch and 1.003 inch; consequently the entire lot is of acceptable quality.

MEASURING VARIATION NUMERICALLY

Elucidating and useful as frequency distribution graphs may be, they do not lend themselves to ready numerical comparison and mathematical handling. The mathematician requires numerical data to work with and to use in comparing essential characteristics of one distribution pattern with those of others. Fortunately such numerical results can be derived from frequency distributions, be they distributions of dimensions, breaking strengths or any other quality characteristics. The two most important values for quality control work which are obtained from frequency distributions are the *average* and the *standard deviation*.

The average, more technically known as the arithmetic mean, is a well known measure, the details of which have been previously presented. The meaning of the standard deviation is somewhat more difficult to comprehend. The standard deviation serves as a mathematical index of the degree of spread or variation of the individual data in a distribution. The greater this spread of data, the larger will be the value of the standard deviation; and the smaller this spread, the smaller will be the standard deviation. The extent of this variation is, of course, dependent upon the variability of the process producing these data. High precision, resulting in only small variability, will produce distributions with only a small standard deviation. Conversely, low precision will result in a relatively large standard deviation.

It will be realized, of course, that part of the observed

standard deviation of a distribution is not caused merely by the variability of the process but also by the variations contributed through imperfect measuring methods and equipment. Since these two basic causes are practically inseparable, references to the standard deviation or variability of a process tacitly assume that inherent in such data are the additional but equally important differences due to the measuring process.

CALCULATING THE STANDARD DEVIATION

For a full appreciation of the way in which the standard deviation provides a relative index of variability, an example of its calculation may be studied.

Let us assume that we have performed tests on a Rockwell Machine to determine hardness of 126 steel blanks, all produced in one heat and from reasonably uniform raw material. The test results are as follows:

Reading Obtained on Rockwell "C" Scale	No. of Blanks (Frequency)
41	1
42	2
43	5
44	15
45	25
46	30
47	25
48	15
49	5
50	2
51	1
Total	126

Thus one blank showed a hardness of 41, two blanks showed a hardness of 42, five blanks showed a hardness of 43, etc. To better visualize the data, they may be presented in the form of a frequency distribution graph as shown in

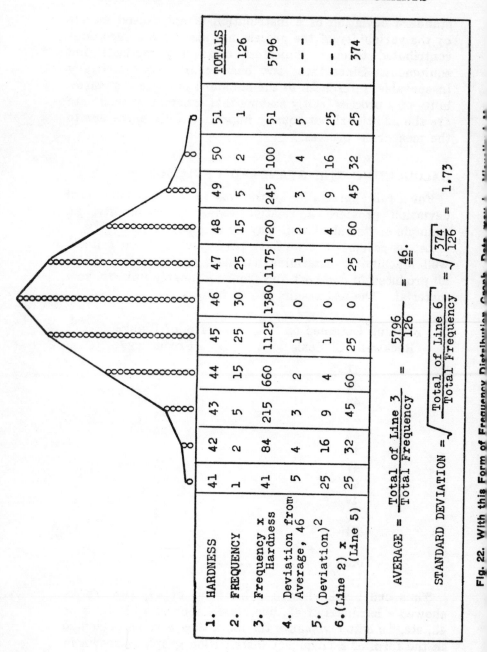

	41	42	43	44	45	46	47	48	49	50	51	TOTALS
1. HARDNESS	41	42	43	44	45	46	47	48	49	50	51	
2. FREQUENCY	1	2	5	15	25	30	25	15	5	2	1	126
3. Frequency x Hardness	41	84	215	660	1125	1380	1175	720	245	100	51	5796
4. Deviation from Average, 46	5	4	3	2	1	0	1	2	3	4	5	--
5. (Deviation)^2	25	16	9	4	1	0	1	4	9	16	25	--
6. (Line 2) x (Line 5)	25	32	45	60	25	0	25	60	45	32	25	374

$$\text{AVERAGE} = \frac{\text{Total of Line 3}}{\text{Total Frequency}} = \frac{5796}{126} = \underline{46.}$$

$$\text{STANDARD DEVIATION} = \sqrt{\frac{\text{Total of Line 6}}{\text{Total Frequency}}} = \sqrt{\frac{374}{126}} = 1.73$$

Fig. 22. With this Form of Frequency Distribution Graph, Data may be Visually Ana...

Fig. 22. The horizontal line represents the hardness scale, from 41 to 51. The vertical columns represent the number of blanks having each degree of Rockwell hardness. Thus 30 blanks showed a hardness of 46, 25 blanks a hardness of 45, etc. These facts are again shown numerically in line 2 of the graph, labeled "Frequency." In practical inspection work, the readings obtained will rarely be distributed as symmetrically as in this example, which purposely presents an ideal case in order to afford better opportunity of observing certain characteristic features of frequency distributions.

A glance at the graph will reveal that the distribution is centered symmetrically about the hardness value of 46. This is the average; however, if the distribution were not symmetrical we could not obtain the average merely by visual examination, but would have to compute it. The method of computation is shown on the graph. Each Rockwell hardness number on Line 1 is multiplied by its frequency, Line 2. The result is written in Line 3, "Frequency $\times$ Hardness." To illustrate: $41 \times 1 = 41$; $42 \times 2 = 84$; $43 \times 5 = 215$, etc. The total of all entries in line 3 is 5796. Dividing this figure by the total frequencies, line 2, we

obtain $\dfrac{5796}{126}$ or 46. This is the *average* of the distribution, often written $\overline{X}$ and pronounced "X-bar."

The remaining three lines in Fig. 22 are used to compute the standard deviation of the distribution. In line 4, the deviation of each Rockwell Hardness from the average is shown. Thus Rockwell Hardness 41 differs by 5 from the average, 46; Rockwell Hardness 42 differs by 4 from the average, 46; etc. Next the deviations are squared, giving the values shown in line 5: $5^2 = 25$, $4^2 = 16$, etc. The last line gives the result of multiplying each figure in line 2 by the figure in line 5. Thus, $1 \times 25 = 25$; $2 \times 16 = 32$; etc. The total of the last line is 374. We now have all the totals from which to compute the standard deviation by applying the formula:

$$\sigma = \sqrt{\frac{\text{Sum of "Frequency} \times \text{Deviations}^2\text{"}}{\text{Total Number of Cases}}} \quad (1)$$

The symbol σ ("sigma") is the conventional abbreviation for the term "standard deviation." Substituting in the above formula, we obtain for our particular example,

$$\sigma = \sqrt{\frac{374}{126}} = 1.73 \quad (2)$$

The value 1.73 is the standard deviation of the distribution. It is a numerical measure of the degree of spread or variation in a set of data. Thus if another distribution has a standard deviation of approximately 1.73 we would know

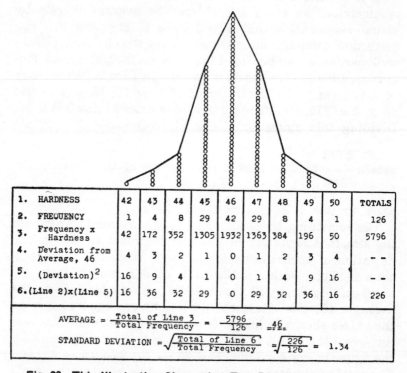

1.	HARDNESS	42	43	44	45	46	47	48	49	50	TOTALS
2.	FREQUENCY	1	4	8	29	42	29	8	4	1	126
3.	Frequency x Hardness	42	172	352	1305	1932	1363	384	196	50	5796
4.	Deviation from Average, 46	4	3	2	1	0	1	2	3	4	- -
5.	(Deviation)^2	16	9	4	1	0	1	4	9	16	- -
6.	(Line 2)x(Line 5)	16	36	32	29	0	29	32	36	16	226

$$\text{AVERAGE} = \frac{\text{Total of Line 3}}{\text{Total Frequency}} = \frac{5796}{126} = 46$$

$$\text{STANDARD DEVIATION} = \sqrt{\frac{\text{Total of Line 6}}{\text{Total Frequency}}} = \sqrt{\frac{226}{126}} = 1.34$$

Fig. 23. This Illustration Shows that Two Distributions with the Same Average May have Different Standard Deviations. Compare with Fig. 22 Having the Same Average but a Larger Standard Deviation.

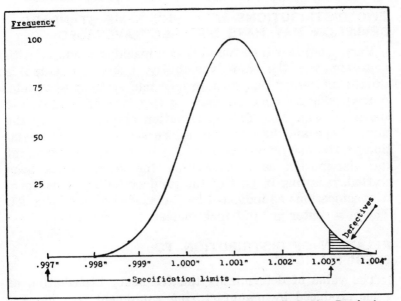

Fig. 24. Frequency Distribution Curve Showing Defective Product Due to Improper Centering about the Nominal Dimension of 1 Inch (Compare with Fig. 21).

that it had been produced by a process with the same variability. If a third distribution has a significantly smaller or greater standard deviation, it gives evidence of less or more variability, respectively.

TWO DISTRIBUTIONS WITH THE SAME AVERAGE MAY HAVE DIFFERENT STANDARD DEVIATIONS

The average and the standard deviation are independent measures. Each particular distribution has its own standard deviation, and two distributions having the same average may yet show entirely different standard deviations. To illustrate this fact, Fig. 23 has been drawn, showing a distribution with average of 46 and a standard deviation of 1.34. This distribution has the same average as the one previously shown (Fig. 22), but its standard deviation is smaller. This indicates less variability, a fact which is not only borne out by the smaller value of the standard deviation but also by the smaller spread of the distribution.

TWO DISTRIBUTIONS WITH THE SAME STANDARD DEVIATION MAY HAVE DIFFERENT AVERAGES

Very often it will be found that a machine produces with approximately the same variability, but the *average* is shifted off center due to improper tool setting, wear, etc. A frequency distribution showing this type of condition is shown in Fig. 24. This distribution exhibits exactly the same shape and has, therefore, the same standard deviation as the one shown in Fig. 21; however, the center of the distribution as measured by the average has been shifted, resulting in part of the product failing to conform to specifications as indicated by the shaded area of Fig. 24. The new center is 1.001 inch instead of 1.000 inch.

RELATION OF DISTRIBUTION TO SPECIFICATIONS

The value of determining the frequency distribution of a lot produced by manufacturing equipment becomes apparent, since it can be determined from this distribution whether or not any product falls outside the specification limits. Thus Fig. 21 shows a distribution which conforms fully to the requirements of the tolerance. Fig. 24 presents a distribution which contains defective product due to a right-axis deviation of the average, which may be the result of improper setting, wear, etc. Fig. 25 shows a distribution which is properly centered but contains defective product due to excessive variability, as shown by the standard deviation of the process. This may be caused through loose or worn parts, or inherent lack of adequate precision. Information obtained from frequency distributions is valuable, therefore, not only in knowing whether a process is producing defectives or not, but also in what direction corrective action must be taken—centering of process or reducing variability.

IMPORTANCE OF STANDARD DEVIATION AND AVERAGE

The significance of the standard deviation and average in quality control is that once these two values are known,

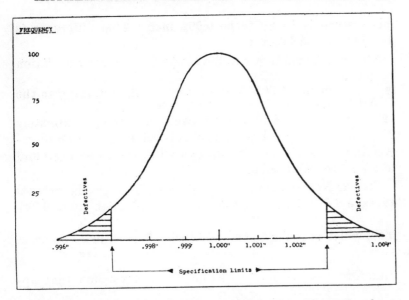

Fig. 25. The Distribution Represented by This Illustration is Properly Centered but there is Defective Product due to Excessive Variability.

(or can be estimated with the necessary degree of reliability) they give valuable information about the distribution in relation to the specification limits. Thus it becomes possible to estimate, from small samples, the distribution of the lot and to know whether or not in all likelihood defective product is being produced.

Let us assume that a certain cylindrical part is required to be ground to a diameter of 1 ± .003 inch. Analysis of a few sample results leads to an estimate of the standard deviation of the process of 0.0025 inch and an estimated average dimension of 1.001 inch. The latter is called the "process average" to distinguish it from "sample averages." The question may now be posed: "Is this lot satisfactory? If not, what is the percentage of defectives?" This question can be answered in a practical manner by means of the following simple arithmetic:

Step 1: Determine the difference between the process average 1.001 inch and the upper specification limit, 1.003

inch, which is found to be 0.002 inch. This difference is denoted by the letter t.

Step 2: The ratio of t to the estimated standard deviation is $\dfrac{0.002}{0.0025}$ or 0.8. This is the ratio $\dfrac{t}{\sigma}$. By referring to the value closest to 0.8 in Table 9, we find that approximately 20 percent of the cylinders probably have an outside diameter in excess of 1.003 inches and will have to be reground to a smaller dimension.

Step 3: Now determine the difference between the process average 1.001 inch and the lower specification limit 0.997 inch, which is found to be 0.004 inch. The ratio $\dfrac{t}{\sigma}$ becomes therefore $\dfrac{0.004}{0.0025}$ or 1.6. From Table 9 we find that approximately 5 percent of the product probably falls under the lower limit and will have to be scrapped.

Step 4: The percentage of cylinders to be reground is 20 percent, and the percentage to be scrapped is 5 percent.

The conclusions just arrived at could hardly have been anticipated or determined quickly without use of the mathe-

Table 9. Percent Defective Product Corresponding to Computed Values of t ÷ σ

$\dfrac{t}{\sigma}$	Percent Defective	$\dfrac{t}{\sigma}$	Percent Defective
**	50% (or more)	1.60	5%
0.50	30%	1.75	4%
0.85	20%	1.85	3%
1.00	16%	2.05	2%
1.15	12%	2.30	1%
1.25	10%	2.55	0.50%
1.40	8%	3.05	0.10%
1.55	6%	3.10	††

**Values ranging from zero to minus-values may be obtained in computing $\dfrac{t}{\sigma}$.

††The Percent Defective is practically zero.

matical method just shown. If, instead of an outer dimension, an internal diameter is involved, then the pieces outside the upper specification limit are scrap and tnose outside the lower limit are in need of rework. For many types of product the division into scrap and rework will not be applicable and all the defectives will be of just one kind.

Now let us assume that on another quantity of cylinders the process average is 1.002 inch and the standard deviation 0.0002 inch. Is that lot satisfactory or not? Applying the method just shown to the upper tolerance limit, we find

$$t = 1.003 - 1.002 = 0.001, \quad \frac{t}{\sigma} = \frac{0.001}{0.0002} = 5.$$ Table 9

indicates that for a value of 5, the defective product occurring is 0. Since the process average is closer to the upper limit than to the lower limit, it is evident that with no product outside the upper limit the probability is that there will also be none outside the lower limit.

It is important to note that the process average in the second example is closer to the tolerance limit than in the first example; yet the second lot was satisfactory whereas about 20 percent of the first lot were oversize and 5 percent were under the lower limit. The reason is found in the fact that the standard deviation of the first lot was considerably greater than that of the second lot. Thus both average and standard deviation are needed to judge the quality of a lot. An examination of Table 9 will reveal that in order to be practically sure that no defective product is in a lot, the ratio $\frac{t}{\sigma}$ should be equal to or greater than 3.1 with respect to both upper and lower limits.

COMPUTING THE CONTROL LINES

The value 3.1 just referred to suggests that control limits might be obtained merely by drawing a line which is 3.1σ above the lower specification limit and 3.1σ below the upper specification limit. This would be correct *if we could be*

*sure that every sample average is the correct estimate of
the process average.* However, since the sample average is
based on inspection of only a very few sample pieces, an
allowance must be made for sampling errors. If this allowance is not made, we will frequently reject perfectly good
lots merely because our sample, by chance, happened to
consist of units whose average was poorer than the process
average. A practical allowance, such as is used in this book,
is one that involves a maximum risk of making an error
2 or 3 times out of 100, because of sampling fluctuations.
In other words, up to 3 times in 100 when the control chart
indicates that trouble exists in the process, none will
actually be found. This looks like a large margin of error;
but it should be remembered that only small samples are
being inspected. Also lots will usually be better than just
borderline in acceptability, in which case the probability of
sampling errors becomes progressively smaller with the
improved quality of each lot.

The factor used in making this allowance for sampling

errors, equals $2 \dfrac{\sigma}{\sqrt{n}}$. This mathematical expression is ex-

plained in Chapter 15. The n in this formula refers to the
sample size. The value of this allowance for sampling errors
is deducted from the previously given figure 3.1. To obtain a
Lower Control Limit (L.C.L.) we merely apply the formula:

$$\text{L.C.L.} = \text{Lower Spec. Limit} + 3.1\sigma - 2\frac{\sigma}{\sqrt{n}}. \qquad (3)$$

The method for Upper Control Limits is similar.
Formula (3) above may also be written, more simply:

$$\text{L.C.L.} = \text{Lower Spec. Limit} + (3.1 - \frac{2}{\sqrt{n}})\,\sigma. \qquad (4)$$

For a lower Specification Limit of .997″, a standard deviation of .0005″, and samples of size 4, the L.C.L. becomes

$$\text{L.C.L.} = .997 + (3.1 - \frac{2}{\sqrt{4}})\ .0005 = 0.998 \text{ inch}$$

This is a method which has been used frequently in calculating control limits, but it is too involved to be very practical; therefore a simpler method which has been developed is found in the practical part of this book. Instead of the standard deviation, the *average of a series of sample ranges*, designated as the "Process Variability" is computed. There is a close relation between the Process Variability and the standard deviation, which is presented in the following table:

If Sample Size is	To Obtain Standard Deviation, Multiply Average Range by
2	0.89
3	0.59
4	0.49
5	0.43
6	0.40
7	0.37
8	0.35
9	0.34
10	0.33

The term Average Range used in this table is an abbreviation of "average of a series of sample ranges."

This table may be used readily to find the standard deviation of a process. For example, if $n = 4$, we obtain

$\sigma = 0.49\overline{R}$, where $\overline{R}$ represents the Average Range.

Let us now return to the quantity $(3.1 - \frac{2}{\sqrt{n}})\ \sigma$ given

in Formula (4). For samples of size 4, this quantity becomes

$$(3.1 - \frac{2}{\sqrt{4}})\ 0.49\overline{R} = 1.03\overline{R} \tag{5}$$

Since the coefficient of $\overline{R}$ is 1.03 for a sample size of 4, or approximately 1, this permits disregarding it without introducing errors of practical importance.

By repeating our evaluation in a similar manner for sample sizes 3 and 5, it will be found that the coefficients of $\overline{R}$ also are close enough to 1 to permit them to be disregarded. Therefore $\overline{R}$ alone can be used in connection with specification limits to find the control limits as shown in Chapter 4. This simplification in the practical computation of control limits makes shop applications less complicated and thereby permits wider use of control charts.

OPERATING CHARACTERISTIC CURVES

Our discussion of control charts for averages in Chapter 4 would not be complete without presenting also their operating characteristic curves. These curves are similar to those shown previously for sampling plans, and are furnished in Fig. 26 for sample sizes of from two to ten.

To illustrate the use of these curves, let us assume that we are testing six sample pieces every hour from a production process. Assume further that the production within that period contained 2.5 percent defectives. What is the probability that our control chart for averages will indicate this process to be out of control?

Entering the chart at the 2.5 percent defective point along the bottom, we proceed vertically until the curve for samples of size 6 is reached. On this level, to the right, we find 80 percent on the vertical scale reading "Percent of Rejections." This means that about 80 percent of the time, our chart would have rung the "out-of-control" bell.

Should this 80 percent be considered inadequate, then the sample size will need to be increased. As the chart shows, by increasing the sample size to 8, our probability of an individual sample ringing "out-of-control" would be close to 90 percent. Further, by stepping up the sample size to 10, a 2.5 percent defective production run would be shown as a "maverick" about 95 percent of the time.

Many a conscientious inspector may worry that the degree of control afforded by the control chart is not close enough.

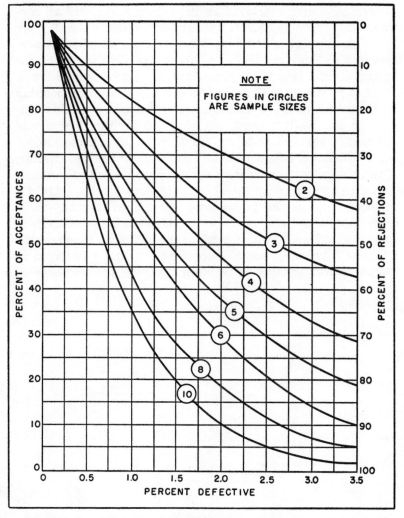

NOTE
FIGURES IN CIRCLES
ARE SAMPLE SIZES

Fig. 26. Operating Characteristic Curves for Control Charts for Averages.

He may argue: "Did you not say that a control chart can often predict impending trouble *before* actual defectives make their appearance? And here I see that even if there *are* actual defectives, the control chart may still occasionally "accept" the production run!"

Such inspector overlooks an important feature of all control charts; namely, that the chart also reveals a trend, from one plotted point to the next. Now, if a series of successive averages shows a tendency to cluster too close to one of the control limits, this is an indication to us that something is about to go wrong with the process. We are then in a position to do something about it immediately. Because of this feature of the control chart, our true sampling risk should in practice stay much below our theoretical expectation.

An additional means of close control is, of course, attained in those applications where a range chart is used in conjunction with an averages control chart. Operating characteristic curves for range charts cannot be furnished in ready-made form, and are therefore not included in this book. Such curves would need to be computed individually, based on the Process Variability and the specification limits involved in the particular product to be controlled.

PART II

Additional Quality Control Tools

14

Further Discussion of Product Variability

For the majority of industrial quality control uses, the Average Range and the Standard Deviation are the most suitable and popular measures of variability. These have been discussed in the preceding chapter.

Another yardstick of variability, which is often very useful especially in the processing type of industries, is the Coefficient of Variation. It is a relative measure, expressing variability as a percentage of the average and is used in comparing such characteristics as tensile strengths, weights of material and other data where it is applicable.

COMPUTATION

Prior to going into the practical applications of the Coefficient of Variation, we should first become familiar with its very simple computation. As an example, we may refer to Fig. 22, page 112, which shows the frequency distribution of hardness readings on metal blanks. The basic data are: Distribution Average, 46. Standard Deviation, 1.73. To find the Coefficient of Variation, V, we write:

$$V = \frac{1.73}{46} \times 100 = 3.76 \text{ percent.}$$

Proceeding in a similar manner for the data in Fig. 23 on page 114, with an average of 46 and a standard deviation of 1.34, we find a Coefficient of Variation of 2.91 percent.

Thus the Coefficient of Variation of a series of measurements or other tests is merely the Standard Deviation of these data divided by the average.

PRACTICAL APPLICATION

In certain applications, the Coefficient of Variation is a more meaningful measure of variability than the Standard Deviation. For example, the owner of a weaving mill had his cloth weights checked over a period of months and obtained the following results on two styles:

	Style A	Style B
Average weight per yard, in ounces	10	15
Standard Deviation, in ounces per yard	0.3	0.3

From an examination of the Standard Deviations, it would appear that on both styles the mill had been equally successful in maintaining good control over cloth weights — an important factor from both a cost and quality viewpoint. Yet, when the Coefficients of Variation were computed, they revealed a different picture:

	Style A	Style B
Coefficient of Variation, in percent	3	2

Thus, it was shown that the *relative variability* of Style B was less than that of Style A. In actual figures, Style B exhibited only a 2 percent coefficient while Style A showed 3 percent.

The example above is a simplified version of a mill experience involving not just two but about a dozen styles. This mill, by comparing the Coefficients of Variation for all major styles, was able to isolate those cloths where variability was relatively excessive. This in turn led to corrective action in spinning, yarn preparation and weaving where required.

WHEN TO USE THE COEFFICIENT OF VARIATION

The principle brought out in this illustration applies to all cases where variability of product may be expected to increase proportionately to increases in the average weight, strength, or other characteristics measured. Often a relatively excessive variation, not revealed by the Standard Deviation, is brought to light very forcefully when revealed in terms of Coefficient of Variation.

You may ask: "Why not use the Coefficient of Variation in all cases?" Unfortunately, this cannot be done. For in many cases the Coefficient of Variation may be misleading, especially in dimensional quality control problems. For example, the problem of machining a certain part to a basic dimension of, say, 15 inches is in no way different from that for another part of, say, 10 inches. Therefore, the Standard Deviation alone should be used to express variability.

Thus, before using the Coefficient of Variation we must assure ourselves that this is really the type of measure which will be most meaningful. The test of its applicability will always be: May we normally expect the variability of the particular product involved to increase proportionately to increases in the average weight, strength, or other characteristic measured?

PHYSICAL MEANING OF STANDARD DEVIATION

The Standard Deviation or Coefficient of Variation, whichever you use, has a definite and important physical meaning. This meaning may be derived from a study of the normal bell-shaped curves and the so-called "normal laws" developed therefrom.

To visualize this meaning, we may artificially construct a perfectly normal distribution, taking as a theoretical example a series of hardness readings on a lot of metal blanks, as shown in Fig. 27.

The average of this distribution is 45, and the Standard Deviation is 1.0. Now, according to the normal laws it has been established that within a range of 45 ± One Standard Deviation there will be 68 percent of all metal blanks. In other words, this percentage of blanks will fall in the range 44 to 46. Now within a range of 45 ± Two Standard Devia-

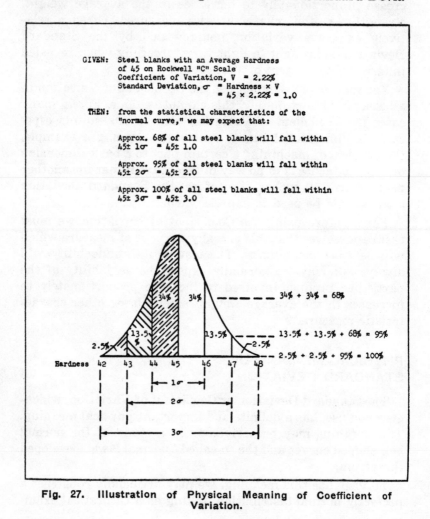

Fig. 27.   Illustration of Physical Meaning of Coefficient of Variation.

tions there will be found 95 percent of all metal blanks. This covers the values 43 to 47 along the bottom scale. Finally, within a range of 45 ± Three Standard Deviations, which is from 42 to 48, there will be found 99.7 or practically 100 percent of all the metal blanks in the distribution. If we are looking at only one side of the distribution, the aforementioned figures of 68, 95, and 100 percent would be halved to 34, 47.5, and 50 percent respectively.

The practical significance of the relationships within a normal distribution, such as shown in the example above, is that it holds true regardless of whether we are dealing with metal blanks, or yeast cell counts from a fermentation process, or viscosity readings or any other variable. If a particular distribution is approximately normal, and we know its Average and Standard Deviation or Coefficient of Variation, then we will find to either side of the distribution average approximately 34 percent of all individual units within One Standard Deviation, 47.5 percent within Two Standard Deviations, and about 50 percent within Three Standard Deviations.

The number of pieces falling inside and outside various ranges of from 0.1 to 3.0 Standard Deviations are shown in Table 10, "Areas Under the Normal Curve."

PRACTICAL APPLICATIONS

The importance of Table 10 will be demonstrated in many uses to be given in further portions of this book. As a matter of fact, the table has been applied previously, in Chapter 13, although at that time we were not yet ready to refer to it by name. These uses were as follows:

1. In Table 9, page 118, there are given values of Percent Defective Product with special reference to an illustration of grinding. Using Table 9, the number of cylinders to be scrapped or re-ground was estimated. It will be seen that this table is based on data similar to that given in the first and third columns of Table 10. (Actually, Table 9 was derived from a more detailed table of areas under the normal curve, and because of the rounding of data and a slightly different

Table 10. Areas Under the Normal Curve

Range of Stand-ard Deviation*	Percent of Pieces Falling Within this Range†	Percent of Pieces Falling Outside this Range†
0.1	4	46
0.2	8	42
0.3	12	38
0.4	16	34
0.5	19	31
0.6	23	27
0.7	26	24
0.8	29	21
0.9	32	18
1.0	34	16
1.1	36	14
1.2	38	12
1.3	40	10
1.4	42	8
1.5	43	7
1.6	45	5
1.8	46	4
1.9	47	3
2.0	47.5	2.5
2.6	49	1
3.0	50‡	0‡

*Range to either side of the distribution average.

†In place of the term "pieces," the terms units, articles, items, values, observations, or measurements may be substituted, depending upon the particular use of the table.

‡Actually, these values are 49.9 and 0.1, respectively.

Example 1: To find the percent of pieces falling within a range of 1 Standard Deviation on either side of the Distribution Average, read 34 percent in the second column opposite 1.0 in the first column. Since under the Normal Curve 50 percent of the pieces lie on either side of the Distribution Average, 50 — 34 or 16 percent of the pieces fall outside of a range of 1 Standard Deviation on either side of the Distribution Average, as shown in the third column.

Example 2: As shown in the second column, 49 percent of all pieces fall within a range of 2.6 Standard Deviations on either side of the Distribution Average and, as shown in the third column, 1 percent falls outside.

emphasis of use, the two Tables 9 and 10 do not completely match in all entries.)

2. In Chapter 13, under the section, "Computing the Control Lines" (see page 119), we multiply the Standard Deviation by 2 in order to assure a risk of not more than 2 or 3 out of 100 (or in other words, 2.5 percent) that a sample average will erroneously fall outside one of the control limits. Here again, the value 2 was taken from Table 10; for opposite this value, in the first column we find the figure 2.5% in the third column, which is the risk sought.

TESTING FOR NORMALITY

Often it becomes important to test a distribution for normality, that is, whether it conforms more or less to a normal curve. Here again, Table 10 may be used. As an example, we may refer to the data on hardness of 126 metal blanks in Fig. 23, page 114, showing an average hardness of 46 and a standard deviation of 1.34.

From the normal probability law, we would expect that in the hardness range of 46 to 47.5 there will be found 45 blanks. This is computed as follows:

1. The difference between 47.5 and 46 is 1.5.

2. This 1.5 divided by the Standard Deviation of 1.34 gives a Standard Deviation range of 1.12, or say, 1.1.

3. From Table 10, 1.1 is found to correspond to 36 percent of a distribution.

4. This 36 percent applied to the total of 126 blanks is 45 blanks.

Now let us check whether the actual distribution conforms to the theoretical 45 blanks. We note that within the hardness group labeled 46, but actually ranging from 45.5 to 46.5, there are 42 blanks. Therefore, from 46 to 46.5 we can count only half of this, or 21 blanks. Proceeding further, from 46.5 to 47.5 (designated in the chart as 47), we note there are 29 blanks. Now, 21 blanks plus 29 blanks gives us a total of 50 blanks for the range from 46 to 47.5. This figure of 50 may be said to agree reasonably close to the theoretical 45 shown above. So far, our distribution is therefore fairly normal.

Next we proceed to find the group in the hardness range from 46 to 48.5. Again our theoretical computations show us:

1. The difference between 48.5 and 46 equals 2.5.

2. This 2.5 divided by the Standard Deviation of 1.34 gives 1.9, rounded out.

3. The value 1.9 corresponds to 47 percent in Table 10.

4. This 47 percent applied to 126 blanks gives 59 blanks as the expected number of blanks in the hardness range from 46 to 48.5.

Now, as shown in Fig. 23, the actual number of blanks in this group is composed of the 50 blanks previously determined plus an additional 8 blanks in the range 47.5 to 48.5 (designated in the chart as 48), giving a total of 58 actual blanks. The agreement of this figure with the theoretical 59 is very close.

Proceeding in this manner from one group to the next, both towards the upper and lower limits of the distribution, we thus establish how closely the actual pieces are distributed along the pattern expected from normal chance variations. For the example at hand, we may say that the agreement is good, and our distribution is for all practical purposes normal.

DERIVATION OF NORMAL CURVE

In discussing the physical meaning of the Coefficient of Variation or Standard Deviation in terms of areas under the normal curve, the question comes up as to how this curve is derived. Actually, there are several ways of development, all of which involve quite advanced mathematics. Rather than go into these, an intuitive understanding of the normal curve can be gained from a study of the throws of two dice, as shown in Fig. 28.

While individual distribution of dice throws will vary, the most likely result obtained from thirty-six throws is that presented by the diagram, where two and twelve are least frequent and a seven predominates most of the time. Note that this distribution is beginning to shape itself after the normal-curve pattern. Now imagine that distributions were

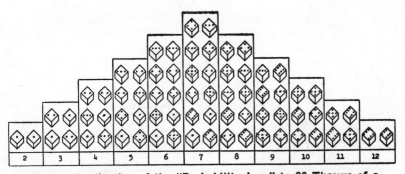

Fig. 28. Application of the "Probability Law" to 36 Throws of a Pair of Dice. Normally, These Thows will Produce the Type of Distribution Presented Above. Where the Basic Distribution of Data in Industrial Testing Approximates This Type of Pattern, Mathematical Probability Laws May be Used to Interpret the Data.

made from the throws of three dice, then four, and so on. Finally, the last and theoretically "infinite" distribution would assume the perfect normal outline.

Some elementary probability calculations become apparent. For example, the odds of throwing "snake-eyes," that is a two, are 1 out of 36 or 1/36. The probability of throwing "snake-eyes" *or* "box cars," the latter being a twelve, is 1/36 plus 1/36 which becomes 1/18. Further, the chance of throwing a seven is as high as 6 out of 36, or 1/6. The chance of throwing two sevens in *successive throws*, is $1/6 \times 1/6$ which is 1/36.

The above examples form the simple laws from which are calculated the various combinations and odds in games of chance, which is indeed the purpose for which the science of statistics was first developed. Today it is finding more fruitful and constructive applications in research, applied science, and industry.

Where the basic distribution of data in industrial testing approximates the so-called normal pattern, as illustrated in Fig. 28, the laws of mathematical probability already discussed may be used to interpret the data. For other than normal distribution, special formulas have been worked out, but since their industrial application is infrequent, they will not be discussed here.

15

Control Charts
Computed from Center Lines

A simple and useful control chart for hardness tests on shovel blades was presented in Fig. 5, Chapter 4. As explained in Chapter 4, this chart was constructed by deducting the Process Variability (Average Range multiplied by adjustment factors) from the maximum specification limit and adding it to the minimum. The resultant values, plotted as two lines on the chart, constituted the control limits.

These limits are suitable for most uses, especially in piece-parts applications. However, in many of the processing type of industries, the concept of a natural individual piece of product is often not applicable, and consequently there are no specification limits for individual items. For example, what yardage length of a large metal coil constitutes a "piece" or "unit of product?" How many gallons or pints or other units constitute an individual item in a tank car of industrial alcohol?

In such cases and in other situations where it is considered desirable, we must work from either the Process Average or nominal standard in constructing control limits. (It should be noted that the term "Process Average" is often replaced by the notation "Grand Average," to emphasize that it is usually computed from a series of sample averages.) When drawn on a control chart, the Grand Average or nominal standard appears as the so-called "center line."

COMPUTATION

The calculation of limits for control charts based upon the Grand Average utilizes the formulas:

Upper Control Limit = Grand Average + (Average Range
   × Factor)

Lower Control Limit = Grand Average — (Average Range
   × Factor)

The factors mentioned in these formulas are tabulated below. They have been so calculated that the control limits involve a maximum risk of making an error only 2 or 3 times out of 100, because of sampling fluctuations. In other words, up to three times out of 100, when the control chart indicates that trouble exists in the process, none will actually be found; but 97 times out of 100 it is likely that something *has* actually gone wrong which needs correction. It will be noted that this interpretation is identical to the one given for the previously presented control charts based upon specification limits.

Sample Size	Factors Used in Computing Control Limits
2	1.25
3	0.68
4	0.49
5	0.37
6	0.32
7	0.28
8	0.25
9	0.23
10	0.20

ILLUSTRATION OF USE

As an example, we may take the data on colorimeter tests on a cola drink, using random bottles taken from one of the bottling lines, tabulated on the next page. The number of bottles per sample, that is the sample size, is three. The Average Range is 5.5 and the process Grand Average is 225.3. We now compute:

1. Average range 5.5 times factor 0.68, equals 3.74.

2. Grand Average 225.3 plus 3.7 equals 229.0. This is the upper control limit.

3. Grand Average 225.3 minus 3.7 gives the lower limit of 221.6.

The resultant control chart appears in Fig. 29. Supplemented by additional controls, such as for specific gravity, it will aid in maintaining a close check over raw materials costs and consumer appeal of the product as regards uniform level of flavoring and coloring.

Daily Colorimeter Test Results on Cola Drink
Bottling Line No. 1

Day	Bottle No. 1	2	3	Sample Average (Rounded Out)	Sample Range
1st	222	228	229	226	7
2nd	223	225	231	226	8
3rd	225	221	223	223	4
4th	222	224	226	224	4
5th	228	226	230	228	4
6th	222	226	224	224	4
7th	228	226	224	226	4
8th	220	218	228	222	10
9th	230	224	225	226	6
10th	224	220	228	224	8
11th	230	224	227	227	6
12th	224	222	226	224	4
13th	227	228	226	227	2
14th	224	222	225	224	3
15th	225	231	227	228	6
16th	226	220	228	225	8
17th	223	227	229	226	6
18th	228	226	224	226	4
19th	226	224	228	226	4
20th	221	229	221	224	8
Total				4506	110
Average				225.3	5.5

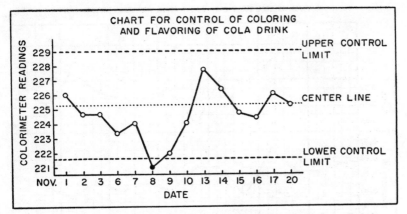

Fig. 29. Chart for Control of Coloring and Flavor of Cola Drink.

MULTIPLE CONTROL CHARTS

As an illustration of the simultaneous control of several characteristics, there is furnished in Fig. 30 the chart for chemical analysis of steel used in tire molds. The molds are cast with a plain surface and the treads are machined afterwards. Therefore, "free machining" sulphur steel is used, and control charts are maintained on the following chemical components:

1. *Carbon:* Must be sufficient to prevent "tearing" of the metal in front of the tool bit, but should not be too high in order to avoid excessive hardness and costly machining.

2. *Sulphur:* Must be sufficient to promote easy machining but yet as low as possible to save processing costs.

3. *Manganese:* Requires close control for reasons similar to carbon and sulphur.

4. *Silicon:* Must be adequate to avoid gassy castings, but yet low enough to prevent excessive de-oxidation, which would increase hardness and machining costs.

The importance and advantage of close control of these characteristics are thus quite apparent. The data presented here are due to Mr. Robert J. Feltrin, of the Quebec Metallurgical Industries, Limited. They represent comfortably

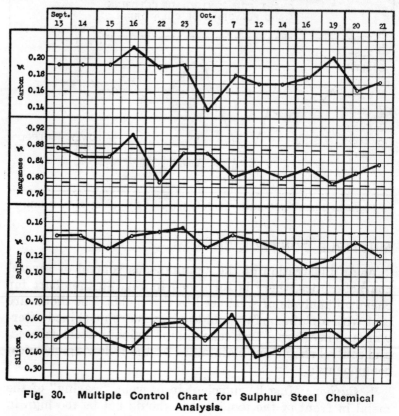

Fig. 30. Multiple Control Chart for Sulphur Steel Chemical Analysis.

narrow limits, achieved by him as a result of his control installation in a Canadian foundry.

CONCURRENT AVERAGE AND RANGE CHARTS

The next illustration shows a set of control charts for both sample averages and ranges, the application being taken from a finishing process on dyed woolen cloth (Fig. 31). The variable to be controlled here is fulling time in minutes, using the following data: Grand Average, 78.0 minutes; Average Range, 13.0 minutes; as derived from the tabulation below. Control limits for sample averages are computed:

Fulling Times for Woolen Cloth, Style 176
(All Readings are in Minutes per Piece)

Batch No.	Observation No.				Sample Average	Sample Range
	1	2	3	4		
1	75	70	75	60	70.00	15
2	65	70	75	85	73.75	20
3	75	75	75	90	78.75	15
4	80	80	75	65	75.00	15
5	85	85	90	85	86.25	5
6	85	70	80	85	80.00	15
7	75	80	65	75	73.75	15
8	80	75	70	70	73.75	10
9	90	80	85	90	86.25	10
10	90	80	80	80	82.50	10
Total					780.00	130
Average					78.0	13.0

1. Average Range 13.0 times factor 0.49 equals 6.4.
2. Upper limit equals 78.0 plus 6.4 or 84.4.
3. Lower limit equals 78.0 minus 6.4 or 71.6.

Next we refer to the method for range control limit calculations from Chapter 5, and multiply: Average Range 13.0 times the constant 2.3, giving a control limit of 29.9, as drawn on the chart.

BASIS OF CONTROL LIMIT FACTORS

The mathematical basis of the factors used in finding control limits for sample averages based on the Grand Average, is developed from the following reasoning:

1. The Standard Deviation of *individual pieces* in a distribution is found by multiplying the Average Range by the conversion factors previously furnished. Now, the Standard Deviation of *sample averages* from a distribution is obviously smaller, since an average is a central value, while the individual pieces may spread over an entire range.

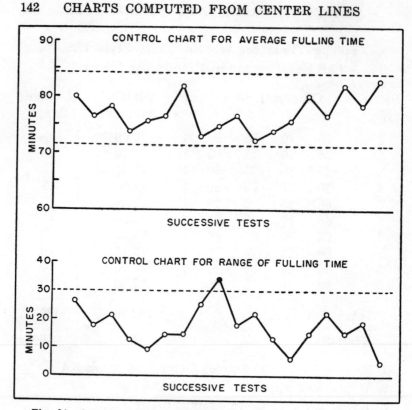

Fig. 31. Combined Average and Range Chart for Fulling Time for Woolen Cloth.

2. From mathematical statistics, we can prove that the Standard Deviation of sample averages from a bell-shaped distribution equals:

$$\frac{\text{Standard Deviation of Individuals}}{\sqrt{\text{Sample Size}}}$$

and is also more briefly called "Standard Error."

3. Table 10. Areas under the Normal Curve (see page 132) shows under Column III that 2.5 percent of all pieces in a normal distribution fall outside the range of 2 Standard Deviations to either side of the distribution average. Similarly, 2.5 percent of all sample averages will fall outside the range of 2 Standard Errors of the distribution average.

4. Therefore, by setting an upper control limit Two Standard Errors above the Grand Average, the odds or chances are only 2.5 out of 100 that a sample average will exceed the control limit, due to the "luck of the draw," in sampling and testing. These odds are identical to those previously explained in developing the modified control limits (see page 133).

5. For a lower control limit, the risk of sampling error is also 2.5 out of 100, similar to the upper limit. Therefore the total sampling risk is 5 percent (2.5 plus 2.5). Actually, of course, a sample average can fall outside *either* the upper limit *or* the lower limit but not outside *both* at one test. Furthermore in most testing, primary interest usually centers towards control of either one of the two control limits. For these reasons, the 2.5 percent risk will generally correspond more closely to actual conditions than the theoretical 5 percent.

6. By utilizing the conversion factors for estimating the Standard Deviation from the Average Range and allowing for two Standard Errors, our last formula becomes:

$$\text{Two Standard Errors} = \frac{\text{Average Range} \times \text{Conversion Factor} \times 2}{\sqrt{\text{Sample Size}}}$$

The factors used in finding control limits for sample averages have been calculated from this formula. The resultant control chart is often said to have "two-sigma" limits, because of the Two Standard Error allowance in this formula.

SPECIMEN CALCULATION

As an illustration of how the factors for control limits are computed, let us follow the steps involved in finding the value for the factor corresponding to a sample size of 9.

1. To convert Average Range to Standard Deviation, based on sample sizes of 9, we multiply the Average Range by 0.34. This was explained in Chapter 13, page 121.

2. Next we find the square root of 9, which is 3.

3. Substituting in the preceding formula, we obtain:

Table 11. Summary of Control Chart Factors

Formula → Sample Size	Control Limits for Averages		Range Control Limit		Conversion of Average Range to Std. Deviation
	Spec. ± Av. Range × F_s	Aver. ± Av. Range × F_a	Aver. Range × F_r		Aver. Range × F_d
	Factor, F_s	Factor, F_a	Factor, F_r		Factor, F_d
2	1.5	1.25	3.27		0.89
3	1.1	0.68	2.57		0.59
4	1.0	0.49	2.28		0.49
5	0.9	0.37	2.11		0.43
6	0.9	0.32	2.00		0.40
7	0.86	0.28	1.92		0.37
8	0.8	0.25	1.86		0.35
9	0.8	0.23	1.82		0.34
10	0.8	0.20	1.78		0.33

F_s = Factor for use in computing control limits on product specification limits. (*See* Chapter 4).
F_a = Factor for use in computing control limits based on process grand average. (*See* this Chapter).
F_r = Factor for use in computing control limit for range charts. (*See* Chapter 5).
F_d = Factor for converting average range to standard deviation. (*See* Chapter 13).

$$\text{Factor} = \text{Average Range} \times \frac{0.34 \times 2}{3}$$

4. The fraction above reduces to 0.23, which is the value shown in the tabulation of factors used in computing control limits given on page 137.

SUMMARY OF CONTROL CHART FACTORS

The various factors for computing control charts, which have been presented in the preceding chapters, are now summarized for convenient use in Table 11. It will be noted that the factors given here for range charts result in slightly different (more refined) limits than those obtained by the simplified method originally furnished in Chapter 5.

———

Note: When it is costly and difficult to make frequent processing adjustments, the use of wider limits, based on 3 rather than 2 standard errors, is often preferred. For such purposes the values from which the factors on page 137 have been obtained are enlarged by multiplying them by 3/2, yielding:

Sample Size	Control Limit Factor
2	1.88
3	1.02
4	0.73
5	0.58
6	0.48
7	0.42
8	0.37
9	0.34
10	0.31

These 3 standard error limits decrease the risk of erroneous rejection to only 0.1 to 0.3%, but involve a correspondingly larger risk of passing off-standard production. (The exact risks depend upon the Operating Characteristic curves, which would have to be constructed individually).

16

Acceptance Control Charts

Where certain items of supply are purchased regularly from one or more sources, control limits may be established to serve as a basis for acceptance or rejection of the items in question. Often, such limits may be set in such a way as to take account of an "Allowable Percent Defective" or, as it is sometimes phrased, "Allowable Percent Non-conforming."

COMPUTATION OF LIMITS

For the calculation of "acceptance control" or "rejection" limits, whichever you may wish to call them, the previously used formula:

Rejection Limit = Specification Limits ± (Average Range × Factor)

is applied.

The factor to be used varies according to the Allowable Percent "Non-conforming" or "Defective" product, as shown in the following table:

Sample Size	Allowable Percent Defective Product						
	Nil	0.5	1.0	2.0	3.0	4.0	5.0
	Factor [1]						
2	1.49	1.03	.81	.57	.41	.30	.20
3	1.14	.84	.69	.53	.43	.35	.29
4	1.02	.77	.64	.51	.43	.36	.31
5	.94	.72	.62	.50	.42	.37	:32
6	.90	.69	.60	.49	.42	.37	.33
8	.84	.66	.57	.47	.41	.37	.33
10	.80	.63	.55	.46	.41	.36	.33

APPLICATION

As an example, we may take the case of a contractor who supplied the U.S. Army Quartermaster Corps with an item known technically as "Barrier-Material, Waterproof, Flexible, Type C-2." The minimum specification for tensile strength in the weaker direction was 36 pounds. Process variability, as expressed in an Average Range of 8.0 based upon samples of six test specimens each, was considered generally satisfactory. The Allowable Percent Non-conforming Product was 5. To compute the lower rejection limit, we proceed as follows:

1. From the preceding table, we find that the factor for sample sizes of 6 and Allowable Percent Non-conforming of 5.0 equals 0.33.

---

[1] The factors are obtained by substituting in Equation 4, page 120, the appropriate value of t/σ from Table 9, in place of 3.1. Thus, 3.1 represents practically 0 percent defectives, but if, say, 4 percent defectives is allowable, then a t/σ of 1.75 would be substituted, as Table 9 shows.

2. Average Range 8.0 times 0.33 gives 2.64.

3. Minimum specification 36 plus 2.64 gives a resultant rejection limit of 38.64.

Obviously, no upper rejection limit is needed, since the higher the tensile strength, the more acceptable will be the product submitted.

QUALITY HISTORY RECORD

From records of inspection over a period of time, the quality history shown in Fig. 32 was built up. Examining the data for the first period, which covers 20 lots, we note the following:

1. The Average Range for samples of six is equal to 8.04 and the Grand Average is 40.0 pounds.

2. The difference between the Grand Average and the specification minimum of 36 equals 4 pounds.

3. This 4 pounds, when divided by the Standard Deviation of 3.2, results in a value of 1.25.

4. Reference to Table 9, page 118, shows that 1.25 corresponds to 10 percent defectives. This represents an estimate of the average percentage of non-conforming product which was submitted by the supplier.

The quality history record thus summarizes the observed data on sample averages and ranges, in addition to furnishing a practical estimate of the average percent defective or non-conforming product submitted by the supplier.

An interesting fact is brought out by the quality history record, when comparing the period of March 17 to 28 against the period April 3 to 11. During both periods, the Grand Average of the process was 41.4 pounds tensile strength. Yet, the Percent of Non-conforming Product decreased in the latter period. As can be seen, this was accomplished by reducing the process variability. This fact emphasizes the importance of uniform production as a means of bringing about quality improvements.

QUALITY HISTORY RECORD

Mill:

Date:

1. Product Barrier Material, Waterproof, Flex.

2. Specification Strength = 36 lbs. in weaker direction

3. Supplier

4. Sample Size 6

5. Factor for converting Average Range to "σ" } 0.40

6. Location

7. Prep. by

8. Dates: From ___ To ___

16. Quality Control Chart

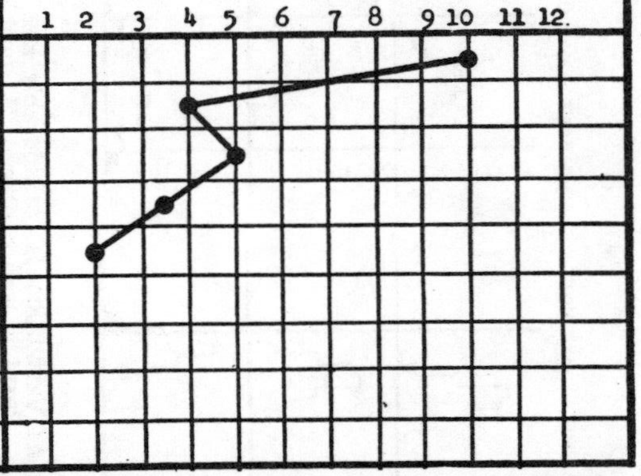

9 Period		10	11	12	13	14	15
From	To	Average Range	Grand Average	"t" (2)-(11) or (11)-(2)	"σ" (5)x(10)	$\frac{t}{\sigma}$ (12)÷(13)	% Nonconforming
2/4	2/16	8.04	40	4.0	3.2	1.25	10.0
2/18	2/29	7.20	41	5.0	2.9	1.73	4.0
3/3	3/14	7.12	40.4	4.4	2.8	1.60	5.0
3/17	3/28	7.45	44.4	5.4	3.0	1.80	3.5
4/3	4/11	6.80	44.4	5.4	2.7	2.00	2.0

Percent Non-conforming Product

Fig. 32. Quality History Record for Waterproof Barrier Material.

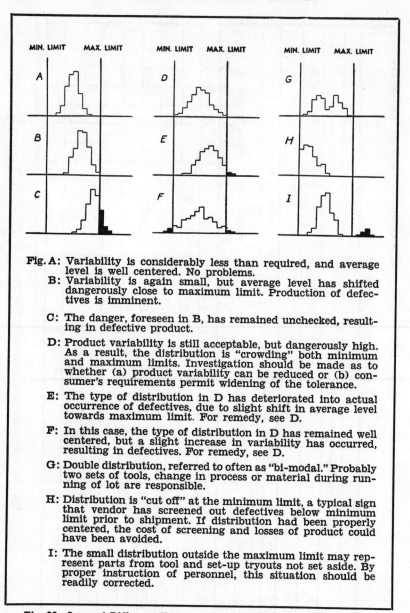

Fig. A: Variability is considerably less than required, and average level is well centered. No problems.

B: Variability is again small, but average level has shifted dangerously close to maximum limit. Production of defectives is imminent.

C: The danger, foreseen in B, has remained unchecked, resulting in defective product.

D: Product variability is still acceptable, but dangerously high. As a result, the distribution is "crowding" both minimum and maximum limits. Investigation should be made as to whether (a) product variability can be reduced or (b) consumer's requirements permit widening of the tolerance.

E: The type of distribution in D has deteriorated into actual occurrence of defectives, due to slight shift in average level towards maximum limit. For remedy, see D.

F: In this case, the type of distribution in D has remained well centered, but a slight increase in variability has occurred, resulting in defectives. For remedy, see D.

G: Double distribution, referred to often as "bi-modal." Probably two sets of tools, change in process or material during running of lot are responsible.

H: Distribution is "cut off" at the minimum limit, a typical sign that vendor has screened out defectives below minimum limit prior to shipment. If distribution had been properly centered, the cost of screening and losses of product could have been avoided.

I: The small distribution outside the maximum limit may represent parts from tool and set-up tryouts not set aside. By proper instruction of personnel, this situation should be readily corrected.

Fig. 33. Several Different Types of Frequency-Distribution Curves. The Shape of the Curve and Its Position with Respect to the Tolerance Limits Provide Important Information on the Quality of the Incoming Parts.

ALTERNATIVE APPROACH

The Acceptance Control chart, in common with all control charts for averages, does not show up sudden increases in variability. Accordingly, you may wish to use also a Range chart to control variability. However, many quality control engineers will still not be satisfied. They argue that, unless close liaison is maintained between vendor and consumer, it will be difficult to assure that each shipping lot is also a "rational" production lot. The importance of rational lots has been stressed in Chapter 2, page 6.

QUALITY REPORT No. 4823

PRODUCT _COMPRESSION SPRING_   CUSTOMER _____   QUOT. No. _87884-8_

CHARACTERISTIC _P @ L OF 0.180"_   PART No. _9008243_   REF. ____

INSP. METHOD _217-PM_   SPECIFIED LIMITS _200 GRAMS ±5% @ 0.180"_

SAMPLE DRAWN _AFTER CAD. PLATE_ EQUIV. INSP. LIMITS _190-210 GRAMS @ 0.180"_

HPS ORDER No.		80710 (15M)	82444 (5M)	
CUSTOMER ORDER No.		116649	117243	
INSPECTED BY		R.H.D E.B.C.	V.G.S.	
DATE		1-6-48 1/7/48	2-9-48	
FORCE (P)		LOT 1	LOT 2	
	MIN.			
190				
2		//	//	//
4		ℍℍ ////	ℍℍ //.	ℍℍ ///
6		ℍℍ ℍℍ ℍℍ //	ℍℍ ℍℍ ////	ℍℍ ℍℍ ℍℍ ///
8		ℍℍ ℍℍ ℍℍ /	ℍℍ ℍℍ ℍℍ ///	ℍℍ ℍℍ ℍℍ ℍℍ ///
200		ℍℍ ℍℍ /	ℍℍ ////	ℍℍ ℍℍ ℍℍ ℍℍ ℍℍ
2		///	ℍℍ	ℍℍ ℍℍ ℍℍ //
4			/	ℍℍ ℍℍ
6				ℍℍ /
8				//
210	MAX.			/
		OK	OK	OK
		8100 PCS.	7M PCS	5100 PCS
		C.J.M.	C.J.M.	C.J.M.

HUNTER PRESSED STEEL CO.
FORM 561—150—12.17.47

Fig. 34. A Quality Report Such as Shown Here is Sent to a Customer with Each Lot of Springs. It Enables Him to Better Adapt His Incoming Inspection Plan for Each Particular Part.

For this, and other practical reasons, many plants do not use Acceptance Control charts. Instead they may favor frequency distribution patterns, such as discussed in Chapters 9 and 13. Such distribution patterns can furnish valuable information about the incoming product, as shown by the typical examples illustrated in Figure 33, and published some time ago in the magazine *MACHINERY*.* Of course, it has been pointed out previously that such distribution patterns are obtained only at the cost of testing 50 to 100 articles per lot, as against only two to ten articles where a control chart is used.

Which technique should you use in your plant? No definite rules can be given. The relative importance of such factors as quality requirements, testing costs and your confidence in the vendor's product should be weighed in arriving at a sound decision. Some progressive vendors, such as the Hunter Spring Company, have furnished their customers with certified frequency distribution graphs, accompanying each lot. For this purpose, a simplified recording form is used, as shown in Figure 34. The particular illustration shows the results on three individual lots, the method of recording being self-evident.

---

*April 1948, page 164.

17

Control Charts
For Percent Defective Product

Control charts for percent defective product represent still another versatile charting tool. The reader may wonder why control charts for percent defective product have not been furnished in the first part of this book. The reason is that in the place of such charts, we can usually apply lot-by-lot sampling plans. The latter have the advantage that they can be listed in ready-made master tables; and where sequential plans are used, they provide the most efficient method of sampling.

Yet, percent defective control charts have their place in modern inspection, because they furnish a continuous visual record of inspection results and quality from hour to hour, day to day and week to week. The decision as to where percent defective control charts should be used can best be made after the principles of their construction and application are understood. To begin, we will examine simple records of defectives.

RECORDS OF PERCENT DEFECTIVE

A typical record of defective product is furnished below for successive lots of a mechanical part. As each lot came off the line, a random sample of 200 articles was inspected, and the results listed:

Lot No.	Defectives in Sample of 200	Percent Defective
1	4	2
2	8	4
3	2	1
4	6	3
5	4	2
6	4	2
7	10	5
8	6	3
9	4	2
10	8	4
	—	—
Total	56	28
Average	5.6	2.8

In the first column, successive lots are listed in numerical order. Next to each lot, the number of defective articles found in each sample of 200 is given. In the third column, these defectives are converted to percent. For example, the sample of 200 pieces from Lot No. 1 showed 4 defectives, or two percent. The average percent defective, p percent, for the ten lots inspected is 2.8.[1] Deducting this figure from 100, we obtain 97.2 as the percentage of articles not defective. In technical language, we may say that this represents the "percent effective" or q percent.

STANDARD DEVIATION OF A PERCENTAGE

We have previously computed Standard Deviations from ordinary series of measurements, or "variables." For percentages, the computation is somewhat different and involves, fortunately, considerably less mathematical figuring.

Referring to the above example of 2.8 percent defectives, 97.2 percent effectives and a sample size of 200, we:

1. Multiply the numerical value of the percent defective by that of the percent effective. Thus we have $2.8 \times 97.2 = 272$.

---

[1] When expressed as a decimal fraction, 0.028, this figure is known as the "fraction defective."

2. Divide this product by the sample size. Therefore $272 \div 200 = 1.36$.

3. Find the square root of the value in Step 2. Thus, $\sqrt{1.36} = 1.17$. This is the Standard Deviation in percent, i.e., 1.17 percent.

The value found in the last step is the Standard Deviation. The method may be summarized in a simple formula:

Standard Deviation of a Percentage $=$
$$\sqrt{(\bar{p}\,\% \times \bar{q}\,\%) \div \text{sample size}}$$

COMPUTATION OF CONTROL LIMITS

Knowing the average and the Standard Deviation of the data under study, we are in a position to compute the control limits. We will recall from our discussion of the physical meaning of the Standard Deviation that 68 percent of all articles in a normal distribution will be found within a range of plus or minus one Standard Deviation to either side of the distribution average. Similarly, 95 percent of all articles will fall within a range of two Standard Deviations; and close to 100 percent will fall within three Standard Deviations. However, in the case of percent defectives we are dealing with what is known as a "binomial," rather than a normal distribution, and therefore the Table of Areas under the Normal Curve does not usually apply.

For binomial distributions, it is customary to use limits based upon three Standard Deviations, applying the formulas:

Upper Control Limit $=$ Average $+$ (3 $\times$ Standard Deviation)

Lower Control Limit $=$ Average $-$ (3 $\times$ Standard Deviation)

Example

For the data presented above, utilizing a sample of 200 articles, 2.8 percent defectives and 97.2 percent effectives, with a Standard Deviation of 1.17%, we proceed as follows:

1. Multiply the Standard Deviation 1.17 by 3, giving 3.5 (rounded out).

2. Add this 3.5 to the average percent defective of 2.8 to obtain 6.3, which is the upper control limit.

3. Subtracting 3.5 from 2.8 gives a minus value, hence the lower control limit is taken as zero.

CONSTRUCTING THE CONTROL CHART

The construction of a control chart, as shown in Fig. 35, from the data just computed is self-explanatory. By plotting

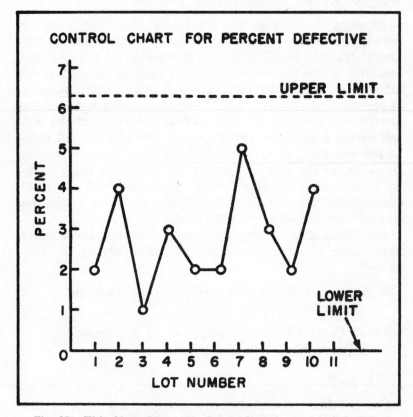

Fig. 35. This Chart Shows No Points Outside the Limit. While This Condition Continues, We May Presume the Production Process to be Controlled.

the inspection results for each lot, it will be noted that all of the lots fall within the control limits. The process from which the samples of mechanical parts were obtained is, therefore, under control.

Where the chart shows that some lots fall outside of the established control limits, indicating that the process is not under control, an investigation into the processing is desirable.

The first aim of the investigation would be to check that inspection and testing are being performed properly and uniformly. Once this is established, the method of sampling should be reviewed, to eliminate the possibility of non-random or otherwise unsatisfactory procedures. As a third step, the processing should be investigated, both as regards general set-ups and the particular occasions when out-of-control points are recorded on the chart.

The same rules for periodic review and recomputation of control limits, as given for control charts for sample averages and ranges, apply also to percent-defective charts. Through use of the charts, improvements in product uniformity should be achieved, which should be followed up with revised and tightened limits where warranted.

PURPOSE OF LOWER CONTROL LIMITS

The lower the percentage defective in a lot, the more satisfied can we usually be with the quality attained. Zero defectives is the ideal attainable. Why then should we provide a lower limit on a percent defective chart?

The reason for a lower control limit is that, when a sample percentage falls below this line, one of the following possibilities may be present:

a. It may be a chance occurrence, due to sampling error. This should happen very rarely.

b. It may represent superficial, careless or altogether improper inspection, which has missed the true high percentage of defective work.

c. It may mean a true lowering of defective product.

The last item bears further discussion. Often, some temporary or inadvertent change in processing may result in better product. And when this is brought to light, due to the sample falling below the lower control limit, it may eventually lead to process changes and permanently improved quality. At other times, a low percentage of defective product may be due to:

a. Raw materials are being used which are too expensive in relation to the quality required, or

b. Equipment may be operating at unduly low speed, resulting in production losses.

Thus, if a quality control program is to be realistic it must safeguard against quality levels achieved primarily at the expense of undue raw materials costs or production losses.

In the computation of control limits, the lower limit may often be found to equal some value close to zero. Sometimes, the calculations may result in a theoretically negative limit, which means that the actual limit should be zero. For such instances, no lower limit line should be drawn on the chart. Similarly, in all those cases where the purpose of such a limit does not appear justified, it should be omitted in order to avoid needless complication of the chart.

CONTROL OF PROCESSING CONDITIONS

The control chart for percent defective may be applied profitably to control processing conditions. A typical example may be taken from woolen yarn spinning. Assume a spinning room containing twelve frames, each equipped with one hundred spindles. At any one time, one or two or more frames may be down for cleaning, changeover, or other causes. In addition, on each of the frames that are running, a number of spindles may be unproductive or "idle" for one of many reasons: mechanical defects, supply run-out not replaced, yarn break not "pieced-up" by operator, etc.

It becomes important to know when the percentage of idle spindles exceeds the allowable limit, so that corrective action can be initiated. A common practice is to make a daily check, of which the following data indicate a typical set of results:

Date	No. of Frames Running	No. of Spdls. On Running Frames	No. of Spindles Idle	Percent Idle
2/1	9	900	12	1.3
2	10	1000	12	1.2
4	8	800	6	0.8
5	11	1100	11	1.0
6	10	1000	10	1.0
7	10	1000	15	1.5
8	12	1200	24	2.0
9	10	1000	10	1.0
11	10	1000	10	1.0
12	10	1000	8	0.8
Average	10	1000		

From experience, a value of one percent for idle spindles is considered standard. We shall use this standard percentage in place of the average percentage. Using the average number of spindles of 1000 on running frames as the sample size, and 100 percent minus 1 percent or 99 percent as the "percent effective," we find the Standard Deviation from the formula:

$$\sqrt{\frac{1\% \times 99\%}{1000}} = 0.3 \text{ percent}$$

Applying our formula for an upper control limit, we have:

Upper Control Limit $= 1\% + (3 \times 0.3\%) = 1.9\%$.

The lower control limit would be found by substituting a minus in place of the plus sign above. This yields a value of 0.1 percent for the lower limit, which may therefore be ignored. The resultant control chart is shown in Fig. 36.

CONTROL CHART FOR NUMBER OF DEFECTIVES

It is sometimes preferable to draw up control charts for the number of defectives found rather than for the per-

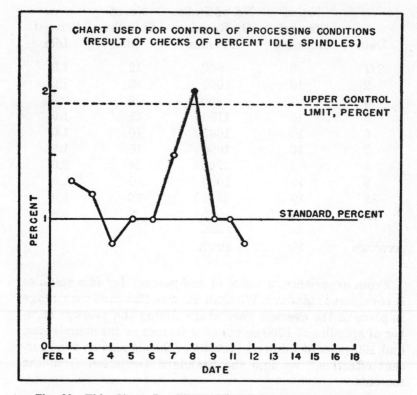

Fig. 36. This Chart Provides a Visual Control Record of Unproductive Spindles in a Yarn Spinning Department. The Out-of-Control Point on February 8 was Traced to Excessive Application of Lubricants by Inexperienced Operator, Resulting in Oily Drafting Rolls and Improper Running Conditions.

centage defective. Such a chart is often more easily understood by production personnel.

For example, in our illustration of mechanical parts, instead of constructing a control chart in terms of percent defectives, we could have constructed simply a chart for "defectives found in each sample of 200." The upper control limit, instead of being 6.3 percent defectives then becomes 6.3 percent of 200 or 12.6 defectives. In actual practice, this means that if up to twelve defectives are found in any sample of 200, the process is still considered in control. However, if thirteen or more defectives are found, the process is considered out of control. Obviously, you cannot find fractional defectives, such as 12.6.

This type of chart is based on the assumption that the sample size always remains constant. In our illustration of mechanical parts, this requirement is met. However, in the case of the example of idle spindles, the sample size did not remain constant. Sometimes only 800 spindles were checked, while at other times 1200 spindles were examined. Now, let us assume we found 10 idle spindles in one day. This represents 1.25 percent of 800 but only .83 percent of 1200 spindles. Accordingly, a control chart of the "number of defectives" type would have been misleading, because it cannot allow in advance for varying sample sizes. Going one step further, it should be pointed out that even a percent-defective control chart is not applicable with fixed control limits wherever the sample size varies more than 20 percent from the overall average. In such a case, individual control limits must be computed for each sample, which becomes very cumbersome in practice. Therefore the quality control engineer will usually seek, as much as possible, to establish conditions that permit use of a sample size that remains fairly constant in percent defective inspection.

CONTROL CHART FOR DEFECTS PER UNIT

The type of chart just discussed should not be confused with the defects-per-unit control chart. The latter is still another variation of the many kinds of control charts in use, and is applied primarily in connection with visual examination of bulky or continuous products, such as belting, cloth or wire cord.

It will be remembered from our discussion on Sampling Continuous Products in Chapter 3 that we may artificially break down uninterrupted lengths of material under inspection into a series of small piece parts, by considering each foot or yard as a unit of product. If we make such a breakdown, then the problem becomes one akin to piece parts inspection, and we may use either a sampling plan or a percent defective control chart. However, many quality control engineers have a preference for a defects-per-unit chart, where "unit" refers to the amount of product sampled.

CONTROL LIMITS FOR DEFECTS-PER-UNIT CHARTS

For the purpose of calculating control limits for the defects-per-unit chart, we first need to know the all-important value of the Standard Deviation. The formula for this is very simple:

Standard Deviation of Defects per Sample =

$$\sqrt{\text{Average No. of Defects per Sample}}$$

As in the case of the Standard Deviation for percent defective, the average defects may represent either a series of actual observations or a desirable standard which is normally considered attainable. In most practical cases, where the production process is not performing "under control" and at the optimum level prior to the use of charts, it will be wise to use the actual average defects as a start. Then, as quality improves, the Standard Deviation should be re-computed based upon the new production level. This process should continue until the desired "standard" is more or less attained or even surpassed.

As an application, we shall consider a sampling of insulated wire, with 50 yards examined from each of ten randomly selected rolls in a lot. From past experience, an average of 2.5 defects per sample of 500 yards is considered normally attainable and has been adopted as standard. To find the control limits, four steps are followed:

1. Compute the Standard Deviation. From the formula above, this simply means finding the square root of 2.5, giving us 1.6 defects as the Standard Deviation.

2. As in the case of percentage limits, we multiply the Standard Deviation by three, giving us 3 x 1.6 defects or 4.8 defects.

3. The upper control limit becomes 2.5 plus 4.8 or 7.3 defects.

4. The lower limit would be found from the computation 2.5 minus 4.8, which gives a theoretical value of less than zero. Since it is an impossibility to ever find less than zero defects, we simply disregard the lower limit on the control chart.

USING THE DEFECTS-PER-UNIT CHART

All uses of the defects-per-unit type of chart run exactly parallel to the ordinary percent defective chart. It will therefore be sufficient here to give just one case history, which happens to come from a bottling plant, and involves an example where a control chart is used as a supplement to 100 percent inspection of the finished bottled product.

In this plant, each bottle passes behind an illuminated magnifying glass. Any foreign matter — such as cigarette ends and a thousand other items thoughtlessly inserted in empty bottles by the public — which may not have been removed in the machine scouring, should be caught in this final inspection. The examiner's job is to remove these and otherwise defective bottles, and set them aside.

At the end of each day, the quality control department receives a small truck containing several cases of rejected bottles, each marked as to the production line from which it came. From production records, the total number bottled on each line is known. Using these two figures, it is a simple matter to compute the number of rejected bottles or "rejects" per shift for each bottling line.

Over a period of time, it is found that 16 "rejects" per shift is the average normally attainable with the type of scouring equipment on hand. The control chart limits are then readily computed as shown below:

1. The square root of 16 is 4. Four rejects per shift is thus the standard deviation.

2. Multiplying by three, as in the preceding example, we find 3×4 equals 12.

3. The upper limit becomes 16 plus 12 or 28 rejects per shift.

4. The lower limit is 16 minus 12, or 4 rejects per shift.

In actual use, an excess of actual rejects over the control limit furnishes a good reason to investigate the scouring operation for wear of brushes, improper settings, and other possible causes. If, on the other hand, the rejects fall below the lower limit, we might interchange inspectors on different lines and see whether the "high quality" follows the inspector. If it does, we may then ascribe this "high quality" to poor inspection.

CONCLUSION

We have discussed the following types of control charts in this Chapter:

Chart for percent defective, also known as the p-chart
Chart for number of defectives, also known as the pn-chart
Chart for defectives per unit, also known as the c-chart.

The view taken has been that the latter two charts are merely variations of the ordinary percent defective chart, even though some of the mathematics is different. Whenever we decide to use any of these charts, we should keep in mind that as an alternative we might use sampling plans. These involve less computation work, but have the disadvantage of not showing the graphic picture of the "status of control" and the quality trend provided by the control chart.

A special use of these charts is in supplementing 100 percent inspection and as a means of controlling processing conditions, as was brought out by the examples of bottling line inspection and idle spindles control in this Chapter.

18

Analysis of Variance

Once we have determined a particular variation, we may find it important to analyze it and break it down into its component individual factors. The fact is that an observed variation usually consists of a set of smaller variations, much in the manner of a famous De Morgan verse, often quoted by statisticians:

> "Great fleas have little fleas upon their backs
> to bite 'em,
>
> And little fleas have lesser fleas, and so ad
> infinitum."

Let us examine how this principle works in industrial statistics.

BREAKDOWN OF VARIATIONS

The fact that an observed variation may consist of smaller individual elements has been brought out previously, such as in Chapter 13 on Mathematical Theory of Control Charts. It was emphasized that the usual method of determining the Standard Deviation of a process tacitly assumes that inherent in such data are the additional variations due to the measuring process. The precision of measurements is never perfect in actual practice, in the same manner as a product tolerance is never zero.

By the use of what is called Variance Analysis, we can isolate and identify the size of the "flea" representing the degree of precision of measurement, and we are then left with the true process variability. Going one step further, however, we can pull another "flea" off the variations due to the precision of measurement. In particular, we can isolate the variations due to the human element, associated with the skill and care of the average tester. As the remainder, we then are left with the inherent precision of the measuring equipment itself, be it a dial gage, a scale or other instrument.

Turning our attention to the process variability itself, we can again break this down into various elements derived from the processing. Some typical applications will be discussed in this chapter. Based on this knowledge, it is often possible to discover hitherto unsuspected causes of product variability and to initiate improvements accordingly. Before discussing how this can be accomplished in actual practice, some basic concepts of Analysis of Variance should first be understood.

THE CONCEPT OF VARIANCE

In statistical quality control language, "Variance" refers simply to the squared Standard Deviation. To take an example from a filtration process, if the Standard Deviation of filtering time for a particular solution is 2.5 seconds per ounce, then the Variance is found to be 2.5 times 2.5 or 6.25 seconds per ounce.

The reason for taking squares is that certain calculations are thereby simplified. To explain this, we may for a moment assume that the reader is already familiar with the technique of Variance Analysis and has found the following Standard Deviations on a certain machine operation:

Standard Deviation Inherent in Machine.......... 6.4

Standard Deviation due to Tool Wear and Setting.. 4.8

Standard Deviation of Bulk Produced, or Overall
    Variation 8.0

All data are in terms of 0.0001 inch. We shall refer to the three types of variation more briefly as Machine, Setting and Overall deviations, respectively. Now, if we express these same data in terms of Variances, we have:

Type	Calculations	Result = Variance
Machine	6.4 × 6.4	41.0
Setting	4.8 × 4.8	23.0
Overall	8.0 × 8.0	64.0

Note that the total of Machine Variance plus Setting Variance, that is 41.0 plus 23.0, equals the Overall Variance of 64.0. This fact usually indicates that our data are correct. Had we performed the same addition on the Standard Deviation figures, we would have had Machine Deviation plus Setting Deviation, or 6.4 plus 4.8, which does *not* equal the true Overall Deviation of 8.0. This phenomenon, which requires the use of squares for addition, is referred to as "Pythagorean" addition, after the ancient mathematician who first discovered this principle when working with triangles.

It is thus shown that if we know two (or more) Variances separately, we can very simply find the Total or Overall Variance by adding the separate Variances. Accordingly, the term "Analysis of Variance" rather than "Analysis of Standard Deviations" is used. It should be emphasized, however, that in many practical process investigations we may find it simpler to deal in straight Standard Deviations or Coefficients of Variations, so long as there is no need to add them.

TYPICAL APPLICATION

Analysis of Variance, especially in industrial research and experimentation, can become a very complex subject. Even as applied to ordinary process investigations, it is difficult to find simple examples. A case history which is believed to demonstrate the basic technique more clearly than any other encountered in the author's experience, is given here. It is taken from a synthetic staple fiber carding and spinning mill, with the following background.

The mill maintained control charts on all major processing operations: carding, drawing, roving and spinning. These charts showed that, beginning with the drawing process, variability of the product as measured in grain weight per yard was very high. Moreover, this high drawing variation was inconsistent with fairly low variation in the carding department. Why should variation jump so suddenly? An investigation was made into the drawing, by checking gear trains, roll settings, weightings and other adjustments, but no cause could be found. An Analysis of Variance, applied to the drawing process, was similarly unsuccessful in finding any possible causes.

Now there exists in a spinning mill a condition commonly encountered in many types of semi-continuous processing. The product from one department is mixed in the processing operation of the succeeding department. In particular, the strands of fibers from about 50 carding department machines will all be routed through one drawing machine. The significance of this is that an excessive *overall* variation in one department will show up as high *machine* variation in the next department. In our particular investigation we want to know: "Is the excessive drawing machine variation caused by an excessive overall variation in carding?"

To test this, the data in Fig. 37 headed "Carding Coefficient of Variation" were obtained. From twelve randomly selected machines, samples of four strands each were taken, weighed, and written down in terms of grains-per-yard. The Range-within was then found for each machine, such as 5.3 for Machine No. 43, 4.1 for machine No. 27, and so on. The total of all these ranges is 54.2 grains; divided by twelve, it gives an Average Range-within of 4.5 grains. Expressed as a percentage of average grain weight of 55.2, this range becomes 8.2 percent. Then, by using our well-known conversion factor for samples of size four, 0.49, we find the Coefficient of Variation to be 4.0 percent. These are familiar computations, and the resultant variation is the Machine Variation, also known as "Within-machine" or "Within-sample" Variation, and the type which is usually represented by range control charts.

To find the Overall Variation, we should now take our 48 test results (twelve samples, four tests per sample), write

Wernertes – P.O.M. Co., N.Y.C.	_Carding_....COEFFICIENT of VARIATION									Form LC-13a

Mill: —	Dept.: Carding	Mach.: Carding		Prep. by: —	Date: —

Item Tested: Grain Weight per Yard	Stock: No. 3				

Yds. Tested: 4 × 5	Doublings: —	Std.: 55.0	High: 52.0	Low: 58.0	Average: 55.2 grs.

Date:	6/1	6/1	6/1	6/1	Range (over-all)					Range (over-all)
Mach. No.	43	27	16	5						
	55.5	51.8	52.0	56.0	4.2					
	60.2	54.2	56.1	57.1	6.9					
	54.8	50.1	54.1	55.2	5.1					
	52.1	54.1	53.0	51.1	3.0					
Range (within)	5.3	4.1	4.1	6.0						

Date:	6/2	6/2	6/2	6/2	Range (over-all)					Range (over-all)
Mach. No.	8	39	7	12						
	50.3	59.9	55.5	58.8	9.6					
	58.8	58.2	50.2	56.1	8.6					
	54.0	56.3	51.6	59.2	7.6					
	53.8	57.0	54.7	57.1	3.3					
Range (within)	6.5	3.6	5.3	3.1						

Date:	6/3	6/3	6/3	6/3	Range (over-all)					Range (over-all)
Mach. No.	21	29	41	32						
	50.4	55.4	58.8	58.6	8.4					
	52.1	56.3	57.3	59.2	7.1					
	51.6	56.1	56.8	55.7	5.2					
	53.5	58.1	53.9	57.1	4.6					
Range (within)	3.1	2.7	4.9	3.5						

SUMMARY	Within	Overall	Notes:
1. Total of Ranges	54.2	73.6	
2. Average Range	4.5	6.1	
3. Average Range, %	8.2	11.1	
4. Coefficient of Variation	4.0 %	5.4 %	
5.			

Fig. 37. Carding Coefficient of Variation.

each on a little slip of paper, and throw them all into a bowl or hat. Then we should draw individual slips, with each group of four representing a new "sample." Taking ranges of these groups of four, we would then be able to determine the Overall Variation of the department. Now in our particular example, both the machines and the individual lengths per sample tested were taken at random and without any significance as to sequence. Therefore, the data are already well enough mixed to obviate the necessity for hat-drawings. Instead, we merely take the Range-across, giving us the Overall Variation. For example, the first line of test results lists, for machines numbered 43, 27, 16 and 5, the data: 55.5 grains, 51.8 grains, 52.0 grains and 56.0 grains. The range of these is 56.0 minus 51.8 or 4.2, as shown on the illustrative form. Proceeding in a similar manner for the next line, we find a range of 6.9 grains. Then, finally, we find a total of ranges equal to 73.6 grains, yielding an average range of 6.1 grains or 11.1 percent (in terms of the average grain weight of 55.2) and a Coefficient of Variation of 5.4 percent. Summarizing, we have found:

Coefficient of Variation, Within Machines........ 4.0

Coefficient of Variation, Overall................ 5.4

Clearly, the Overall Variation is considerably above the Within-machine Variation and must be investigated as the cause of the high variation shown on the control charts for drawing. The actual fault was found to be use of non-standard tension gears, which produced excessive Between-machine Variation, not computed here. The total of the Within-machine and Between-machine Variations constituted the high Overall Variation.

WITHIN-MACHINE AND BETWEEN-MACHINE VARIATION

Wherever there is a processing department in which several machines produce the same material, we must make sure that both Within-machine and Between-machine Variations are kept under control. If we fail in this, then the Overall Departmental Variation will be excessive. How this works is illustrated in Fig. 38.

On the right-hand side of this illustration, we show a typical frequency distribution curve representing the varia-

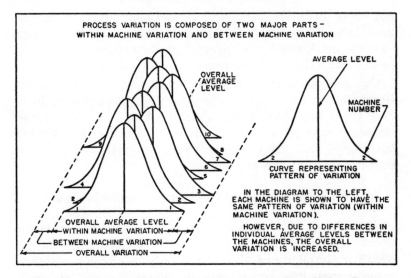

PROCESS VARIATION IS COMPOSED OF TWO MAJOR PARTS —
WITHIN MACHINE VARIATION AND BETWEEN MACHINE VARIATION

**Fig. 38. Process Variation is Composed of Two Major Parts,
Within-machine Variation and Between-machine Variation.**

tion pattern of a machine. The center line in the middle represents the average level. Now let us assume we have several machines in a department, and this frequency curve represents the average Within-machine Variation. For the preceding example, this would mean a coefficient of 4.0 percent. However, due to the fact that not the same tension gears are used on each machine, there is variation in the amount of drafting between the different machines. This results in differences between machine levels, or Between-machine Variation. The left-hand side of our illustration shows how, by displacement of the average level, the individual machines deviate to the right and left. For example, machines No. 3 and No. 7 are far to the right of center, and machines No. 4 and No. 9 are far to the left of center or overall average level. This produces the additional variation shown as "Between-machine Variation" on the chart. The Overall Variation is then the combined total of the Within- and Between-machine Variations.

Where control charts are maintained on individual machines, this situation of excessive Overall Variation would not show up in the particular department involved. It does reveal itself however in that process where the product from several machines in a preceding department is mixed, blended or otherwise combined.

Our last illustration clearly shows that it is a physical impossibility for Overall Variation in a department to be ever truly less than Within-machine Variation. Yet, sometimes you may get a figure for Overall Variation that is below that for Within-machine Variation. When this occurs, several possibilities are present:

(1) An error may have been made in calculations.

(2) The number of samples is inadequate. As a rule you should use enough samples to fill out the entire form in Fig. 37. (For simplicity of illustration, only 12 of the possible 24 samples were used in the example, which is still permissible but not the safest practice.)

(3) Where samples represent routine mill testing results, and possibilities (1) and (2) have been ruled out, we must suspect the performance of the testing. A tester who, under pressure of time or for other reasons skips some tests, is usually good at guessing correct averages, but he would have to be a genius to also make the variations jibe.

EVALUATION OF VARIATIONS

When Overall Variation exceeds Within-machine Variation, this does not necessarily mean that the difference observed is a true one. After all, we have computed the Variation Coefficients from sampling data, and the observed difference in the Variations may be caused by chance fluctuations of sampling and testing. We thus need a method of evaluating the difference in the Variations observed, and to judge whether the excess of Overall over Within-machine may be considered real or ascribable to possible chance fluctuations of sampling and testing. Such an evaluation

Table 12. Values of Minimum Ratios of Variations Needed for Significance

No. of Tests per Sample (Sample Size)	Number of Samples					
	10	15	20	30	40	50
	Values of Minimum Ratios Needed					
2	1.418	1.310	1.253	1.192	1.160	1.140
3	1.211	1.161	1.133	1.105	1.086	1.077
4	1.141	1.109	1.091	1.072	1.061	1.049
5	1.106	1.083	1.069	1.055	1.046	1.041
6	1.085	1.067	1.056	1.045	1.038	1.034
8	1.061	1.048	1.040	1.032	1.028	1.024
10	1.048	1.038	1.032	1.026	1.021	1.019
12	1.039	1.031	1.026	1.020	1.017	1.016
15	1.031	1.024	1.020	1.016	1.014	1.012

Example: Given 10 samples, each consisting of 4 tests. To find Ratio, enter Table at the level of "No. of Tests per Sample (Sample Size)" = 4. Proceed horizontally until column "Number of Samples" = 10 is reached. In the block thus found, the Ratio 1.141 is obtained.

Source: From the author's paper "Variations Flow Analysis" presented in 1956 before the Virginia Academy of Science and subsequently published by the American Society for Quality Control, in "Textile Quality Control Papers," Vol. 4, 1957.

procedure is known as a "significance test." This test may be described by the simple steps shown below, using for illustration the data obtained from Figure 37:

1. Form a ratio of Overall to Within-machine Variation. Thus, for the values of 5.4% and 4.0% for Overall and Within-machine Variation respectively, the ratio is 5.4% ÷ 4.0% or 1.35.

2. Observe that the *sample size* or, in other words, the number of test values used for *each* within-machine range is 4. The *number of samples*, representing the number of groups from which ranges were obtained, is 12. (This is the same 12 which we used to find the Average Range.)

3. Enter Table 12, for sample sizes of 4 and the number of samples closest to 12, which is 10. This shows that the minimum ratio needed for significance is 1.141. Since the actual ratio, from Step 1, is 1.350 and thus greater than the minimum needed, we may consider the excess of Overall over Within-machine Variation to be *significant* (and thus *not* ascribable to chance fluctuations).

In many cases, such as in the example in Figure 37, the differences between the Variations may be so large that no formal significance test is required. Inspection of the results alone will suffice. However, it is often dangerous to rely on such off-hand judgment. Also, where differences are not so clear-cut as in the example, only the ratios in Table 12 can serve as a useful criterion.

As in all sampling, the significance test furnished here involves a certain sampling risk. In particular, the values in Table 12 have been so computed as to involve a risk of 5% of calling an observed difference "significant" when actually it is caused by chance fluctuations of sampling and testing. This appears to be a practical risk for this type of work.

Basis of Nomograph:

(Within-Machine Variation Coefficient)^2 + (Between-Machine

  Variation Coefficient)^2 = (Overall Variation Coefficient)^2

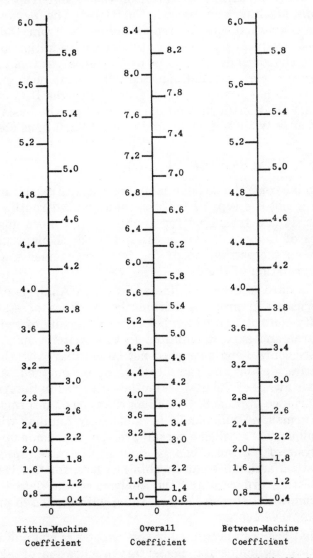

Fig. 39. Nomograph Showing Relationship of Within-Machine, Between-Machine, and Overall Variation Coefficients.

BETWEEN-MACHINE VARIATION

The methods shown above involve the direct determination and comparison of Variation Coefficients representing Within-Machine and Overall Variation. The Between-Machine Variation can be found indirectly from these two values, by means of the "Pythagorean" addition of variances, shown under "Concept of Variance" in this chapter. Based on these calculations, the convenient nomograph in Figure 39 has been prepared, from which the Between-Machine Variation Coefficient can be read on the basis of the particular Within-Machine and Overall Variations observed.

USING ANALYSIS OF VARIANCE

Unlike control charts or sampling plans, Analysis of Variance is not the type of tool that can be used routinely in a plant. It is a technique for analyzing and disentangling a series of individual variances, and much thought must be given to the setting up of the test arrangements and the interpretation of the data.

It is hard to draw the line as to which Analysis of Variance uses fall properly within the province of statistical quality control, and which belong in the realm of industrial research and experimentation. In this writer's opinion, the quality control engineer need not be familiar with the complexities, details and ramifications of the method. As long as he is aware of the basic essentials involved in the Analysis of Variance approach, as well as the type of information it can furnish, he will usually be sufficiently familiar with this technique. Then, when a special problem does come up where Analysis of Variance can be seen as desirable, specialized statistical assistance can be obtained both for the design of the testing program and the analysis of the data to yield information that may have meaning with regard to processing improvements.

What has been presented in this chapter is a simplified yet practical technique for elementary application of Analysis of Variance as a quality control tool in the industrial plant.

19

Statistical Tolerancing

Suppose we are manufacturing three gears of 1-, 2-, and 3-inch face widths, respectively, the gears to be assembled next to each other on a transmission case shaft. If the overall length of the assembled gears must be held within a tolerance of ±0.018 inch, must the tolerance on the width of each of the three gears to be held to ± 0.006 inch or can a larger tolerance be permitted?

The answer given to this question depends, among other things, upon the background of the person of whom the question is asked. A novice in manufacturing practice might say, "To be absolutely sure the assembly will not exceed the ± 0.018 inch tolerance, it is necessary to add the tolerances on the individual widths; therefore, ± 0.006 is the largest tolerance we can afford to give the individual parts since $3 \times \pm 0.006 = \pm 0.018$."

On the other hand, a more experienced observer might say, "It seldom happens that three different parts are all at their maximum (or minimum) dimension at the same time and it is therefore probable that a tolerance greater than ± 0.006 can be applied to each part without exceeding the assembly tolerance of ± 0.018 inch."

It may be seen from these replies that the novice is disregarding extra manufacturing cost and playing 100 per cent safe by specifying a tolerance of no more than ± 0.006

inch while his more experienced friend is willing to gamble that most of the time a tolerance greater than $\pm$ 0.006 inch will not result in more than $\pm$ 0.018 inch in the assembly.

However, this latter viewpoint still leaves unanswered the query "How much more than $\pm$ 0.006 inch can the tolerance be?" It is the purpose of this chapter to provide some of the answers to this kind of question.

The problem of establishing and meeting tolerances in mass production is closely interwoven with the problems of inspection, testing, and control in the manufacturing plant, and it is for this reason that tolerances have received considerable attention throughout this book. In particular, Chapter 7 discusses general principles of tolerances and allowances in interchangeable manufacture; Chapter 9 presents the use of inspection data in establishing specifications; Chapter 13 shows the relation of processing variations to product tolerances; and Chapter 16 depicts the interaction of distribution patterns with tolerance ranges, using several typical examples.

APPLICATION OF VARIANCE ANALYSIS

While the methods described in these chapters were concerned primarily with the evaluation of *individual* tolerances, the present chapter shows how tolerances may be *combined*—other than by simple addition and subtraction—to satisfy a required overall tolerance in assembly. In this work the principles of addition of variances discussed in the preceding chapter may be applied with the result that the final tolerance values established by means of these techniques will permit maximum product variation consistent with quality and processing requirements. Thus, statistical methods can help us to obtain the cost-saving advantages of maximum allowable tolerances consistent with the requisite quality.

VARIANCES IN ACCUMULATIVE ASSEMBLY

When a dimension in an assembly represents a linear combination of several components, it is apparent that the variance in the total dimension is the result of the variances of the parts. Consequently, the relationship between total and individual part variances may be evaluated by means of the statistical techniques of Analysis of Variance.

To illustrate, if the overall dimension of three adjoining gears on a transmission shaft is comprised of three widths of 1, 2 and 3 inches, and each component has been shown from control charts to be normally produced with a standard deviation of 0.002 inch in the width, then the expected standard deviation of the combined dimension, under random assembly, may be determined as shown in Example 1.

Example 1. Linear Combination of Components and Resultant Standard Deviation Obtained from Gear Assembly.

	Gear A	Gear B	Gear C	Assembly
	(Thousandths of an Inch)			
a. Basic Size	1,000	2,000	3,000	6,000
b. Standard Deviation	2	2	2	*
c. Variance ($= b^2$)	4	4	4	12
d. Standard Deviation of Assembly $= \sqrt{12}$				3.46

*Note that standard deviations cannot be added directly. Instead the Analysis of Variance steps in Lines c and d are needed to find the assembly standard deviation.

The steps shown in Example 1 may be expressed in a formula:

$$\text{Assembly Standard Deviation} = \sqrt{\text{Sum of Squares of Individual Standard Deviations}}$$

(1)

Thus, in Example 1,

$$\text{Assembly Standard Deviation} = \sqrt{2^2 + 2^2 + 2^2}$$

$$= \sqrt{12} = 3.46$$

The standard deviation of the combined linear dimensions of the widths will become important when considering the interaction with, for example, a bearing housing on one side and a shaft shoulder on the other.

The data are in terms of 0.001 inch. Formula 1, familiar from Analysis of Variance, is also fundamental to statistical tolerancing. When the standard deviations of the individual parts are identical or approximately alike, the equation simplifies to:

$$\text{Assem. Std. Deviation} = \text{Indiv. Std. Deviation} \times \sqrt{\text{No. of Parts}} \qquad (2)$$

Thus, for Example 1, using units of 0.001 inch,

Assembly Standard Deviation $= 2 \times \sqrt{3} = 3.46$

This simplified formula does not apply where the standard deviations of the components differ. Thus, where the individual standard deviations are 3 and 4, respectively, we would use Formula 1 to get:

Assembly Standard Deviation $= \sqrt{3^2 + 4^2} = 5$

The formula is also valid when variation coefficients are used, since a variation coefficient is merely the standard deviation expressed as a percent of the distribution average. Moreover, the answer just found could have been obtained directly from the nomograph in Figure 39, by drawing a line between the values 3 and 4 of the Within-Machine and Between-Machine coefficients columns, respectively, and reading 5 from the Overall Coefficient column.

REQUIREMENTS FOR FORMULA TO WORK

The relationship of variances in random assembly, shown by Formula 1, will be strictly valid only where the individual parts come from processes under good control, as established from a review of control charts. Such a production process is said to be "in statistical control." It is also desirable that frequency distributions derived from the control chart data be checked, to see that they fall into the approximate pattern of a normal distribution.

Where parts do not come from a process in statistical control, but are thoroughly mixed prior to assembly to assure good randomness, Formula 1 will still be applicable. It has also been demonstrated that the validity of the formula will not be seriously affected when distribution patterns are either much flatter or else much more peaked than the bell shape of the normal curve, shown in Fig. 27, and approach instead an almost rectangular or triangular form. Thus, the relationship depicted in this section should have wide application. Special cases in exception to the general rule will be discussed later.

TOLERANCES IN ACCUMULATIVE ASSEMBLY

In the same way that we can add standard deviations to obtain, by means of the Analysis of Variance formula, an estimate of the overall standard deviation, we can also add individual tolerance values to find overall tolerances. This becomes apparent when one considers that the tolerance is merely another way of stating the allowable standard deviation of product. In particular, when a tolerance is set at $\pm$ 6, then dividing this quantity by $\pm$ the factor 3 from Table 10 of page 132, will yield 2 as the highest allowable standard deviation that can be tolerated without producing defectives.* Conversely, if the standard deviation is 2 for a product obtained from a process under statistical control, then the tolerance which can be maintained by this process is $\pm$ 3 $\times$ 2 or $\pm$ 6. This tolerance represents the capability of the process, and is generally called the "natural tolerance." When this $\pm$ 6 is written in the form of the total spread from $-$ 6 to $+$ 6 around the process average, we obtain the "process spread" of 12 discussed on page 72. This distinction is, however, not a general one; and the term "natural tolerance" is often used indiscriminately to describe either the type of expression shown as $\pm$ 6 or the term shown as 12. The meaning will then depend upon the context.

Using the data from Example 1, we may now show how the same Analysis of Variance formula may be adapted to apply also to tolerances. For this purpose Example 2 is provided. In the example it is assumed that the tolerance specified by the designer is approximately equal to the natural tolerance of the process. Note that Steps d and e represent the same Analysis of Variance procedure as in Example 1, but this time applied to tolerances. Moreover,

---

*Sometimes a more precise factor of 3.1 is used, obtained from data of the type shown in Table 9, page 118. Usually, however, the more convenient rounded value of 3 is considered adequate, since errors in estimating the standard deviation and departures from normality are usually expected to be greater than this small difference of 0.1 anyway—without affecting the practical validity of the factor.

If the Assembly Standard Deviation of 3.46 from Example 1 is multiplied by the tolerance factor of $\pm$ 3 from Table 10, page 132, we obtain the same Assembly Tolerance of $\pm$ 10.4 shown in Example 2. This illustrates the consistency of the two methods.

The formula for Assembly Tolerances is thus:

(3)

Assembly Tolerance =

$$\sqrt{\text{Sum of Squares of Individual Tolerances}}$$

In Example 2,

Assembly Tolerance = $\sqrt{6^2 + 6^2 + 6^2}$ = $\pm$ 10.4

Again, since the tolerances of the individual parts are all alike, we may simplify:

Assembly Tolerance = $\pm$ 6 $\times$ $\sqrt{3}$ = $\pm$ 10.4

Had we used four parts in place of three, all alike as to individual tolerances of 6, we would have had:

Assembly Tolerance = $\pm$ 6 $\times$ $\sqrt{4}$ = $\pm$ 12

Example 2. Linear Combination of Components and Resultant Tolerance, Obtained from Gear Assembly

		Gear A	Gear B	Gear C	Assembly
		(Thousandths of an Inch)			
a.	Basic Size	1,000	2,000	3,000	6,000
b.	Standard Deviation	2	2	2	3.46
c.	Tolerance (= $\pm 3 \times$ b)	± 6	± 6	± 6	*
d.	Squared Tolerance	36	36	36	108
e.	Assembly Tolerance				
	(= $\sqrt{108}$)				± 10.4

*Note that tolerances, like standard deviations, cannot be added directly. Instead, the Analysis of Variance steps in Lines d and e are needed. The Standard Deviation of 3.46 in Line b was obtained from Example 1.

Example 2 assumed the specified tolerance to be approximately equal to the natural tolerance; the formulas shown would work just as well in cases where the specified tolerances are larger than the natural tolerance, so long as each individual tolerance is enlarged by approximately the same proportion. When specifications are wider than existing process capabilities, less frequent machine adjustments, omission of a processing stage, or use of a learner in place of a skilled operator may be considered.

TOLERANCES FOR INDIVIDUAL PARTS

In the preceding sections we have considered the overall tolerance obtained for an assembly, based on the tolerances of the individual parts. Often, however, the problem is reversed: The overall tolerance allowable for an assembly is known, and it is desired to determine the tolerances for the individual parts which, in combination, will yield the allowable overall tolerance. In such cases the individual part tolerance can then be found from Formula 4.

$$\text{Part Tol.} = \text{Assembly Tol.} \div \sqrt{\text{No. of Parts}} \qquad (4)$$

As an illustration, for a specified overall dimension of $\pm$ 5 thousandths of an inch involving four individual component parts, we have:

$$\text{Part Tolerance} = 5 \div \sqrt{4} = 2.5 \text{ thousandths}$$

This formula assumes that all individual part tolerances can readily be made alike. Often, however, this is not the case, as will be illustrated in the example of a plastic coating operation in the next section, showing how an individual tolerance is determined when the overall tolerance and one of two parts tolerances are given.

NON-DIMENSIONAL TOLERANCE ACCUMULATION

We may now examine how the formula for tolerance accumulation works in non-dimensional applications:

Electrical Resistance. In the assembly in series of four resistances, each having a tolerance of 3 Ohms, the resultant combined tolerance is $3 \times \sqrt{4}$ or $\pm$ 6.

Plastic Coating Operation. The tolerance for a coated fabric was $\pm$ 5 tenths of an ounce per yard. The finishing plant was able to maintain a tolerance of $\pm$ 3 for the weight of coating. Therefore, the tolerance for the uncoated material is:

$$\text{Material Tol.} = \sqrt{5^2 - 3^2} = \pm 4 \text{ tenths oz./yd.}$$

The value $\pm$ 4 represents the maximum permissible tolerance for the uncoated material, which must be specified by the finishing plant, if off-standard product is to be avoided.

Airborne Component. Tolerances for weight of an airborne component, consisting of 14 parts, are as follows:

   a. A tolerance of ± 6 oz. for 3 parts.
   b. A tolerance of ± 8 oz. for 5 parts.
   c. A tolerance of ± 4 oz. for 6 parts.

The assembly tolerance is now:

$$\text{Assembly Tolerance} = \sqrt{(3 \times 6^2) + (5 \times 8^2) + (6 \times 4^2)}$$

$$= \pm\ 22.9 \text{ oz.}$$

The relationships demonstrated in the various examples in this Chapter will work, provided the statistically controlled conditions previously outlined are fulfilled within the practical limitations discussed.

THE OLD-TIMER'S OBJECTIONS

The approach to tolerancing shown in this Chapter, using the computation steps borrowed from Analysis of Variance technique, is relatively recent in industry. It has been a natural outgrowth of the use of statistical control charts and related analysis tools. As a matter of fact, the use of the statistical tolerancing approach shown here presumes statistically controlled processing. The rewards for this care and statistical study come in the form of individual tolerances that can be permitted to be wider than otherwise possible, without detracting from the quality of the finished product. This saves production costs. Moreover, when these techniques are used in analyzing fits and clearances, it can often be shown how tolerances can be widened and quality improved at the same time.

The old-timer, however, who has used the conventional additive methods of tolerance accumulation, may well question our Analysis of Variance procedures, arguing like this:

"In the example of tolerance accumulation of three individual parts, each being allowed limits of ± 6 thousandths, you used a formula whereby the final assembly would be expected to be within ± 10.4. Yet, if three parts of + 6 or three parts of − 6 are combined, the limits will become ± 18. This is a lot wider than the ± 10.4 from your formula. Therefore, if parts are at their extremes, the assembly limits would be wider than you predict."

It is true, of course, that when the extremes happen to come together, they will assemble to limits in excess of those given by the square root formula. They will then form the simple additive relation shown in Chapter 7. However, under random assembly such a meeting of extremes may be expected only rarely. After all, extremes form only a very small portion of a bell-shaped frequency curve, and one cannot expect that these few parts will normally meet in assembly. A few such adverse combinations will of course occur. Where distributions are normal and assembly is at random, there will be about three out of every thousand assemblies where the statistically determined tolerance is exceeded in assembly. In practice, due to various inaccuracies and imperfections in requisite conditions, the actual occurrence of assembly failures may be several times greater than the theoretical 3 out of 1000 or 0.3%. Usually, however, this presents no real problems in production, since the operator can break up the adverse combination by simply exchanging the extreme piece picked up last for another random piece from the bench.

While the idea of statistical tolerancing was considered quite revolutionary only a few years ago, there are many plants today that find these techniques essential for their work. It is of course the responsibility of the statistical tolerancing committees in manufacturing plants to recognize those conditions where the prerequisites for the Variance Analysis formula are not fulfilled, and instead the conventional additive or other procedures must be used. This will be discussed at the conclusion of the next Chapter.

20

Additional Applications of Statistical Tolerancing

We will now examine additional uses of the methods of statistical evaluation of tolerances, in order to obtain optimum specifications, beginning with a consideration of fits and clearances.

TOLERANCES FOR FITS

An interference fit between the hole in a gear hub and a shaft involved the dimensions and tolerances shown on Lines a and b of Example 3. The succeeding lines show the determination of the expected tolerance for the fit, using the formula shown in Line e.

Note that the value of 0.0011 inch in the third column represents the fit which occurs when the interfering extremes happen to meet; in particular, a minimum bore diameter assembled with a maximum diameter shaft. However, this is a most unlikely mating under random assembly in mass production. The probable fit for the vast majority of assemblies is defined by the average difference of 5.5 plus and minus the fit tolerance of 4.0, thus giving a range of 1.5 to 9.5 for the expected fit under random assembly.

In practical manufacture, the tolerances for the two parts can thus be opened up, and an effective fit of 0 to 11 would still be maintained. However, the previously stated conditions of statistical control and random assembly must be satisfied. Furthermore, it is important to note that the fit tolerance was computed with regard to individual parts centered at least approximately in the middle of the specification limits. In actual production, this means that the shop must "shoot for the middle" of the part dimensions. The need for such practice becomes apparent wherever processing equipment is used which is just capable or slightly better than required to meet specified limits. Generally, the variability of the items produced from such a process forms the type of distribution pattern described in Fig. 21, page 109, and a shift in the average will result in off-standard parts, as shown in Fig. 24, page 115.

Example 3. Fit Tolerance Resulting from Assembly of Hole and Shaft.

		Hole	Shaft	Interference Fit
		(Ten-Thousandths of an Inch)		
a.	Design Size†	4510	4521	11
b.	Tolerance +	7	0	
	−	0	4	
c.	Average, with Product Centered between Limits	4513.5	4519	5.5
d.	Tolerance from Average ±	3.5	2	
e.	Fit Tolerance $= \sqrt{3.5^2 + 2^2}$			±4.0*
f.	Expected Fit 5.5 ± 4.0			1.5 to 9.5

---

†The design size of a part is that size from which the limits of size are derived by the application of tolerances. If there is no allowance for fit (clearance or interference), then the design size is the same as the basic size.

*Rounded out. This tolerance can be found directly from Fig. 39 by entering the graph at 3.5 and 2.0 at the left- and right-hand scales, respectively, and reading the answer of 4.0 from the center scale.

In those instances where the process variability is relatively small, so that the natural tolerance is markedly narrower than the specified limits, it is no longer desirable to aim production towards the center of the limits. An appropriate shift towards the desirable direction will then usually yield better fits and improved quality.

TOLERANCES AND CLEARANCES

We have just seen how the general formula for combination of tolerances will hold not only for accumulative assemblies but also for interference fits. We will now see

how realistic tolerances can be obtained, using the tolerance formula in clearance fit problems, as illustrated in
Example 4. The data are in terms of 0.0001 inch; and the
expected minimum clearance of 6.8 or 7, rounded out, is
larger by 2 than the allowable minimum clearance of 5.
This suggests that if the mean diameter of the hole were
to decrease by 1, with an increase of 1 for the shaft, thus
using up the approximate difference of 2 between nominal
and expected minimum clearance, no assembly failures
should result.

Example 4.   Clearance Tolerance' Resulting from Assembly of Hole and Shaft.

		Hole	Shaft	Clearance Fit
		(Ten-Thousandths of an Inch)		
a.	Design Size	8000	7995	5
b.	Tolerance +	6	0	
	−	0	6	
c.	Average with Product Centered between Limits	8003	7992	11
d.	Tolerance from Average ±	3	3	
e.	Clearance Tolerance*			
	$= \sqrt{3^2 + 3^2}$			±4.2
f.	Expected Clearance $= 11 \pm 4.2$			6.8 to 15.2

*Since the individual tolerances are alike, we could have used more simply ±3
× $\sqrt{2}$. Here again, the nomograph in Fig. 39 is suitable to find the answer of 4.2.

The effect of such a shift in dimensional averages is illustrated by the dotted frequency distribution in Fig. 40,
which would seem to indicate at first glance that off-
standard product does occur, since 2.5% of the holes and
2.5% of the shafts infringe on the minimum clearance
specified.* This first impression is, however, erroneous
since in actual assembly most of the oversize shafts (between − 4 and− 5) will usually meet with holes of + 1
and wider, thus preserving the minimum clearance of 5. A
similar effect may also be expected for the undersize holes.
A small percentage of less than allowable clearances will
of course occur, and this may be determined as shown next.

*The reader can readily check these percentages, by use of the methods shown in
connection with Table 9, page 118 or the more detailed Table 10, page 132.

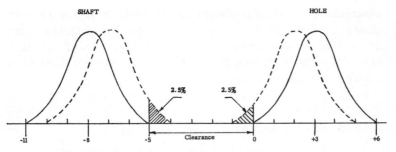

Fig. 40. Distribution of diameters of a hole and a shaft.

DETERMINING EXPECTED FAILURES

In illustrating the method of determining expected failures in minimum-clearance problems, we may utilize the hole and shaft data from our last example, again in terms of 0.0001 inch. Four steps are involved:

1. *Find the Standard Deviation of the Clearance.*
   Since the clearance tolerance is 4.2, division by our (previously discussed) tolerance factor of 3 yields an estimated standard deviation of 1.4.

2. *Determine the Average Clearance.*
   With a shift in dimensional averages by +1 and −1 (7993 and 8002), the old average clearance of 11 has now narrowed to 9.

3. *Determine the "t" of Table 9.*
   The difference between the required minimum clearance of 5 and the average clearance of 9 represents a t of 4.

4. *Look up t/σ in Table 9.*
   The ratio t/σ is now 4/1.4 or 2.9, which is shown from Table 9 to represent 0.1 to 0.5% assembly failures.

The percentage of cases in which minimum clearances will not be fulfilled is thus negligible for most practical purposes. Similarly, it can be shown that the maximum clearance limitation of 17 can be met, with practically no assembly failures.

Effect of Change in Clearance on Rejects. Let us assume that as a result of field experience with the hole and shaft assembly it is found desirable to reduce the maximum clearance from 17 to 13 while still maintaining the minimum clearance of 5 and the standard deviation of 1.4. How many rejects would be found among assemblies that were already completed?

Prior to the shift in averages just discussed in Example 4, we would have expected the following failures with regard to the new maximum clearance limitation:

$$\frac{t}{\sigma} = \frac{13 - 11}{1.4} = 1.43 = 8\% \text{ Assembly Failures.}$$

Subsequent to the shift in averages, we obtain

$$\frac{t}{\sigma} = \frac{13 - 9}{1.4} = 2.9 = 0.1 \text{ to } 0.5\% \text{ Assembly Failures.}$$

It is thus evident that, for minimum and maximum limits of 5 and 13, the design specifications based on the closer distribution averages of 8002 for the hole and 7993 for the shaft would be preferable for any new assemblies. In particular, they avoid the 8% assembly failures just demonstrated for the wider averages.

NOMOGRAPH OF EXPECTED ASSEMBLY FAILURES

Expected assembly failures, such as just discussed, may be determined directly by means of the convenient nomograph in Figure 41 by Dr. J. N. Berrettoni (first published in Automotive Supplement No. 1 by the American Society for Quality Control). Thus, for our example of a maximum allowable clearance of 13 and an average clearance of 11, we enter the nomograph on the t-scale for $t = 13 - 11$ or 2. Connecting this 2 with the value 4.2 on the clearance tolerance scale, we cross the diagonal line, representing expected assembly failures at 8 percent. Thus we would expect 8% of the assemblies to have clearances in excess of the maximum allowed by the tolerance.

As a further illustration, for a minimum clearance of 9, an average clearance of 11, with a resultant t of 2 (as in the case above), and again with a clearance tolerance of 4.2, we would again find 8 percent—this time representing the assemblies with clearances narrower than allowed by the specified minimum of 9. It is obvious that where the minimum clearance is 0, the nomograph will yield the expected percent of interferences.

The nomograph is thus useful in showing expected percentages which will exceed the maximum allowable clearance or fall below the minimum, as well as the expected interferences in assembly. The graph is based on the calculations shown in the preceding section.

COMBINATION OF ACCUMULATIVE AND CLEARANCE TOLERANCES

We are now ready to examine a case history involving both accumulative and clearance tolerances, in Example 5.

Example 5. Clearance Tolerance Resulting from Assembly of Bearing, Snap Ring, and Groove

		Bearing	Snap Ring	Bearing + Ring	Groove Width	Clearance
		(Thousandths of an Inch)				
a.	Basic Size	730	120		853	
b.	Tolerance +	0	2		3	
	—	6	2		0	
c.	Maximum	730	122	852	856	
	Minimum	724	118	842	853	
d.	Mating of Extremes			852	853	1
				842	856	14
e.	Average with Product Centered Between Limits	727	120	847	854.5	7.5
f.	Tolerance from Average ±	3	2		1.5	
g.	Clearance Tolerance $= \sqrt{3^2 + 2^2 + 1.5^2}$					±3.9
h.	Expected Clearance $= 7.5 \pm 3.9$					3.6 to 11.4
i.	New Average for Groove	727	120	847	853	6
j.	Widened Groove Tolerance ±	3	2		3	
k.	New Clearance Tolerance $= \sqrt{3^2 + 2^2 + 3^2}$					±4.7
l.	Expected Clearance $= 6 \pm 4.7$					1.3 to 10.7

Lines a to d show the conventional determination of the expected accumulation of tolerances for a bearing and snap ring, and the resultant extremes of minimum and maximum clearance within a groove. The statistical calculations, in Steps e to h, show that the actual clearances may be expected to range from 3.6 to 11.4, as compared to the conventional range of 1 to 14.

Now, it was found that it would be extremely costly to maintain a tolerance of ± 1.5 on the groove dimension. From the statistical analysis, it was therefore proposed to shift the average groove dimension from 854.5 to 853 and open up the tolerance to ± 3. As shown in Lines i to l, the effect of this change is to maintain a practical range of clearances of 1.3 to 10.7, which represents a generally superior fit at a wider and therefore less costly groove dimension tolerance.

Here again, the old-timer's objections had to be answered. For obviously, if the extremes meet, there will be interference of metal. For this purpose, the old-timer agreed that one might assume that the individual parts could be classified into groups, based on the individual tolerance values, as follows:

Average Minus	Plus	Bearing	Snap Ring	Groove
3		724	—	850
2		725	118	851
1		726	119	852
0	0	727	120	853
	1	728	121	854
	2	729	122	855
	3	730	—	856

Since there are seven bearing dimensions, seven groove dimensions and five ring dimensions, the total of possible combinations in assembly is 7 × 7 × 5 or 245. Yet, only four of these combinations would yield interference. These are:

Bearing	Snap Ring	Bearing + Ring	Groove
729	122	851	850
730	121	851	850
730	122	852	850
730	122	852	851

These four represent just slightly more than 1½% of the 245 combinations and would occur very rarely in practice, since the number of extreme dimensions in each product distribution is only a small fraction of the total product.

The nomograph in Figure 41, which takes into account the fact that the proportion of extremes in each normal distribution is very small, and that each distribution has

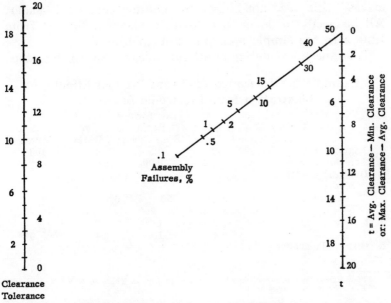

Fig. 41. Expected assembly failures.

really a much finer breakdown of dimensional groups than in the simplified tabulation above, shows that for the example at hand no interferences may be expected from a practical viewpoint.

TOLERANCES FOR COMPLEX COMBINATIONS

The assemblies presented so far involved simple linear combinations. Sometimes, however, tolerances must be considered resulting from assemblies involving products or quotients.

An illustration of tolerances derived from assemblies involving products is shown in Example 6, where the output voltage of a circuit is the cross-product of the input voltage and the effects of the transformer and amplifier. With the exception of Line c, the steps are self-explanatory by following the basic pattern described in previous examples. In Line c, a multiplication is performed using the figures from Line a. While this step actually is a procedure from calculus for obtaining so-called "partial derivatives," this need not bother the non-mathematical reader. All he needs to do is to substitute his own figures from Line a in the simple multiplication in Line c.

Tolerances involving quotients are evaluated by steps

Example 6. Tolerance for Cross-Product Effects, Illustration from Electronic Assembly

	Input Voltage	Transformer Ratio (Step-Down)	Amplifier Ratio	Output Voltage
a. Nominal	50	0.5	4	100*
b. Tolerance ±	1.0	0.005	0.08	
c. Derivative with respect to nominal value	0.5×4 $= 2$	50×4 $= 200$	0.5×50 $= 25$	
d. b × c	2	1	2	
e. (d)^2	4	1	4	9**
f. Output Tolerance $= \sqrt{9}$				±3

*Found from the cross-product of all entries in Line a. Thus, 50 × 0.5 × 4 = 100.
**The sum of the entries in Line e.

Example 7. Tolerance for Quotients, Illustrated from Chemical Finishing Operation, Dyeing of Plastics

	Dye in Dye Bath Per Cent	Dye Absorbed by Product Per Cent	Efficiency of Absorption Per Cent
a. Average	4.0	3.0	75*
b. Tolerance	±0.1	±0.2	
c. Derivative with Respect to Average	$100(-\tfrac{3}{4}{}^2)$ $= -18.75$	$100(\tfrac{1}{4})$ $= 25$	
d. b × c	±1.875	±5.0	
e. d^2	3.516	25.0	28.5**
f. Tolerance $= \sqrt{28.5}$			±5.3

Notes:
*Determined from 3.0 ÷ 4.0 expressed as a per cent.
**The sum of the entries in Line e.

parallel to those for products. An illustration from a chemical finishing operation is given in Example 7, in which the reader can again substitute his own data to obtain the answer sought.

EVALUATION OF MECHANISM RELIABILITY

A special aspect of tolerances, which has gained prominence particularly in the electronics and missile industries, is reliability evaluation. Here, reliability usually refers to the likelihood of non-failure in the performance of an item. Thus, if a part has a reliability of 0.99 or 99%, this means that past experience with the particular product indicates that it will function properly 99 times out of 100, with one failure per 100.

Problems of reliability are especially urgent in complex assemblies, consisting of large numbers of intricate parts. Thus, if a mechanism has 400 parts, each of which has a reliability of 99%, then the assembled mechanism will have a reliability of $(0.99)^{400}$, which comes out to an unacceptably poor 2%! (The statistical basis of this type of calculation was demonstrated in Chapter 12.) No one would, in general, accept a mechanism with a 98% expectation of failure. Manufacturing methods must be such, therefore, that most of the parts have a reliability which for all practical purposes is 1.0, with only a few items of lesser reliability. Thus, the reliability of the entire mechanism may be:

Mechanism Reliability $= 1.00^{397} \times .99^1 \times .98^2 = 95\%$

Much of the work in reliability engineering consists of isolating the type of parts which have relatively low reliability, and seeking corrective means to bring mechanism reliability up to the required standard.

USE OF ELECTRONIC COMPUTERS FOR STATISTICAL TOLERANCING

In those cases where assemblies are relatively complicated, such as in the case of eccentric locations and mounts, the statistical formula for tolerance evaluation may become quite cumbersome. It is then preferable to feed the actual frequency distributions of the component parts into an electronic computer, then let the machine combine the parts data at random, and write out the resultant frequency distribution of the assembly.

A typical problem of this nature is illustrated in Figure 42, for the frequency distribution (A) obtained by random combination on a computer of the patterns of eccentricities (B) and (C). In imitating or "simulating" random assembly on the computer, a set of random angles and cosines was incorporated in the program. The resultant distribution obtained represents the pattern which may be expected in actual assembly. This illustration is due to Mr. R. L. Thoen, staff engineer, General Mills Incorporated, and to *Machine Design* who kindly granted permission for its use.

SPECIAL TOLERANCING PROBLEMS

Despite the wide use and applicability of the general statistical tolerancing formula, there are some exceptions. These occur primarily when distribution patterns are lopsided or "skewed." When skewness occurs, the distribution does not exhibit symmetry, and a "tailing out" towards either extreme side occurs. For example, all three distribution patterns in Figure 42 show marked skewness towards the high side. The general Analysis of Variance formula presented will then be inapplicable, and statistical analysis in general will become quite complex. We then have only one of two choices:

1. Allow for tolerances of assemblies by means of simple (non-statistical) additive procedures.
2. Seek to predict the probable distribution pattern of the assembly, by means of the computer simulation discussed above.

Where access to a computer can be had. the second method will generally be found to be relatively inexpensive in relation to the benefits obtainable from tolerances that are as realistic as feasible.

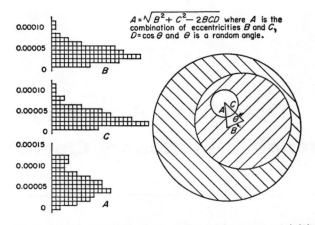

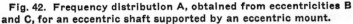

Fig. 42. Frequency distribution A, obtained from eccentricities B and C, for an eccentric shaft supported by an eccentric mount.

The problems presented by skewed distributions are the reason why the reader has been advised to check frequency patterns, obtained from routine control chart data. In many instances, such as production involving eccentricities, radial play, screened and sorted product, or small lots, a check of distribution patterns is especially advisable. In other cases, where experience has shown that skewness need not be expected, a check of frequency patterns may be deemed superfluous. Often, of course, a check of frequency distributions will reveal skewness where none ought to be, such as for example in certain dimensions of ball bearings, thus indicating where production needs to be corrected.

The task of reaching optimality in tolerancing is thus part of an effective overall quality control program for the plant. Ultimate costs are greatly affected by the care which has gone into establishment of proper specifications and tolerances for the components of mass production. As pointed out by Earle Buckingham: "There is probably no other place in the organization where so much money can be saved by careful attention to detail, and there is certainly no other place where so much money can be wasted by carelessness and ignorance."*

*"Dimensions and Tolerances for Mass Production," The Industrial Press, New York 13, N. Y., page 17.

21

Optimizing Processing
Through Evolutionary Operation

Evolutionary Operation is a special technique for the step-by-step improvement of a process, until it reaches an optimum level, resulting in enhanced quality, lowered costs and increased yield.* The method is applied to daily production by introducing a series of systematic small changes in the levels at which process variables are held. After each set of changes the results are reviewed and new changes made, seeking through this evolutionary development to gradually "nudge" the process into optimum operating levels. A simplified example, taken from the sizing of plied synthetic filament yarns, will illustrate how Evolutionary Operation works.

EXAMPLE OF EVOLUTIONARY OPERATION

The primary purpose of the sizing operation is to condition the filaments for weaving so as to minimize yarn breakage and hence maximize weaving efficiency. Existing mill practice involved settings yielding 6 per cent moisture content and 2 per cent elongation of the yarn, which is shown as set-up 1 in Figure 43. It was decided to check this condition against the additional set-ups 2 to 5 indicated on the diagram. These further conditions represent small changes, which were considered adequate to produce dis-

*Developed by G. E. P. Box, Imperial Chemical Industries Limited, first published in *Applied Statistics*, Vol. 6, No. 6, 1957.

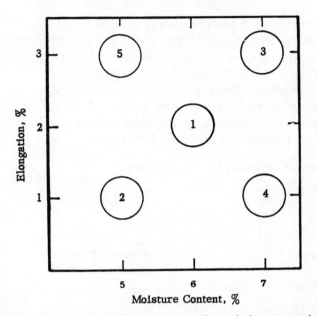

Fig. 43. Design of investigation, comparing existing processing set-up 1 against set-ups 2 to 5. Set-ups are shown in circles.

cernible effects on weaving efficiency, yet small enough to assure that no undue production or quality problems would arise.

Each set of operating conditions was run four times, resulting in four cycles, with weaving efficiencies as shown below:

	\multicolumn{5}{c}{Set-Ups}
	1	2	3	4	5
	\multicolumn{5}{c}{Efficiencies, Per Cent}
Cycle I	91	93	94	98	92
II	94	95	95	97	93
III	94	92	95	96	92
IV	93	96	96	93	91
Average	93	94	95	96	92
Range	3	4	2	5	2

The average of the ranges is 3.2. Since each of the set-up averages is based on four determinations, we enter at this level Table 11, page 144, to find under column F_a the control limit factor of 0.49. Therefore, ± 0.49 times 3.2 or ± 1.6 represents the extent of two standard errors[1] around the set-up average, in per cent weaving efficiency. We may call this ± 1.6 more simply the "error limit."

The relative effects of moisture and elongation are estimated from the arrangement below, in which the set-up averages are recorded to correspond to the relative positions of the set-ups given in Figure 43.

Elongation Per Cent	Moisture Content, Per Cent 5	6	7	Average	Effect of Elongation
3	92		95	93.5	
2		93			− 1.5
1	94		96	95.0	
Average	93.0		95.5	94.25	

Effect of
Moisture   + 2.5

The effect of elongation, − 1.5 in per cent weaving efficiency, is found by subtracting the elongation average of 95 from the elongation average 93.5. By similar subtraction of 93.0 from 95.5 for the moisture averages, the effect of + 2.5 of moisture content is found.

The observed effect of moisture, + 2.5, is well in excess of the error limit, ± 1.6, and indicates strongly that increased moisture content of the yarn is beneficial for weaving efficiency. The observed effect of elongation, − 1.5, is slightly below the error limit, but still large enough to suggest that reduced elongation is beneficial. In general, an observed effect which is below the error limit but still exceeds half its magnitude, may still be considered suggestive of a true effect. However, the smaller the observed effect in relation to the error limit, the greater is the probability that it may represent merely chance fluctuations of sampling and testing.

It is also interesting to compare the efficiency of set-up 1, 93 per cent, against the average of 94.25 per cent for

[1]The reasons for using two standard errors here are the same as those for control chart purposes, as discussed in Chapter 15.

set-ups 2 to 5, which shows that the Evolutionary Operation just completed in its first phase has benefited and not harmed efficiency. A further evaluation may be obtained of the effect of interaction of moisture and elongation, by subtracting the average of set-ups 4 and 5 from the average of set-ups 2 and 3. In particular, 94.5 minus 94.0 yields 0.5, which is a negligible effect by comparison against the error limit of ± 1.6.

We are now ready to decide on the next phase of Evolutionary Operation. Based on the observed effects, a good decision for further evolutionary changes in processing would be as follows: Run a further phase of four cycles. Select the center point, representing the new set-up 1 at a somewhat higher moisture content of 6.5 and slightly reduced elongation of 1.5 per cent. Set up further processing conditions 2 to 5 at spacings of 1 per cent elongation and 1 per cent moisture in a symmetrical pattern parallel to that of Figure 43, but centered around the new set-up 1. Then, after this new phase of operations has been completed, the results can be reviewed again and further phases planned accordingly.

Once experience has been gained with this type of operation, the program may be expanded. Additional criteria of processing cost and product quality may be included. Further processing variables, such as roll pressures, speeds and drying rates, may be incorporated in the investigations.

LABORATORY OPTIMIZATION

It might be argued that Evolutionary Operation during production is relatively slow, and that optimum levels of variables might best be established in the research laboratory. Unfortunately, however, it is usually impossible in the laboratory to satisfactorily duplicate plant conditions, and the optimum level of actual production will therefore differ from the theoretical level predicted. The laboratory works out new processes and procedures and establishes levels which serve as starting points. Evolutionary Operation then investigates successive modifications of the variables, with the objective of bringing the process to optimum levels.

PART III

Reliability

22

Evaluation of Reliability

"The most nerve wracking part of any space flight is the fact that your life depends on thousands of critical parts, each produced by the lowest bidder."

This comment, quipped by an astronaut, is a nutshell evaluation of an intense quality assurance problem: How to enhance reliability of equipment by minimizing the possibility of malfunctions. It is not just in space vehicles, however, that reliability is essential. For example, a large-scale computer consisting of many thousands of critical parts, cannot be permitted to have undue breakdowns. Yet, with growing complexity and increasing numbers of critical parts, electronic computers, automation machinery, and many consumer products, are becoming more and more subject to malfunction problems. There is a great need for thorough and effective quality control in the production of such equipment. Reliability assurance, however, goes a step beyond quality control by providing engineering proof of the performance capability of products.

The problems of reliability in complex systems, such as missiles and electronic equipment, have been mentioned briefly on page 195, Chapter 20. We may re-state in more precise terms the nature of Reliability as the probability that *a product, device or equipment will give failure-free performance of its intended functions for the required duration of time*. While reliability as such is not new, the concept of assessing it in quantitative terms with a conscious engineering effort towards reliability improvement has been with us for only a short span of years.

TYPES OF FAILURE

Sound evaluation of reliability begins with a consideration of the types of failure that may be encountered. Engineers generally have defined three types of failure:

Early Failures. These are the failures resulting from production defects or other deficiencies. Usually, they will show up relatively early in the life of a product. The practice of "debugging," "shake-out" and "burn-in" on new products and equipment is designed to discover and correct such deficiencies.

"Chance" Failures. These are failures that may occur at various intervals during the life of an equipment. Hidden defects that escaped the "early failure" period may result in malfunction later. Environmental stresses, such as electrical, magnetic, temperature or vibration effects, may at times interact in such a manner as to cause component parts and thus the system as a whole to fail. The term "chance" refers to the fact that a particular failure is relatively unexpected. The rates at which such failures are likely to occur, however, have been studied for many components, sub-systems, and equipments as a whole. Fortunately, these rates are quite low in the vast majority of components. Otherwise our modern complex technology would be impossible.

People sometimes say that there cannot be any such thing as a "chance" failure, because every malfunction or breakdown has a cause. True enough, there is such a cause. But it is often extremely difficult to trace it, especially when failures occur at such rare intervals as once every 100,000 or million hours. Yet, we are concerned about these failure rates, since failure of one among many thousands of components in a complex system may bring about system failure. We continue to seek means of reducing chance failure rates to the extent practical, feasible and economical.

Wear-Out Failures. This is probably the most inevitable of all types of failures. Examples abound. Abrasion may cause piston rings, cylinders, valves and bearings to break or function unsatisfactorily. Fatigue or creep of metal, chemical decomposition and corrosion, radiation damage and vibration all take their toll on product life. Wear-out failure occurs when the effect of wear interferes with the intended applications of an object.

For a typical cycle of failures, the fate of humans is often given as a telling example. In the very early stages of life, birth defects cause a relatively high mortality. Then for many decades, the death rate remains relatively low and stable, with only occasional "chance" failures from accidents or relatively rare illnesses or diseases. Then, as we approach later years the "wear-out" stage takes its toll.

Let us examine an automobile tire. Early failures may represent major defects in production, resulting in rejection before sale or else in unsatisfactory performance during the first few days or weeks of use. Thereafter, a tire is likely to run trouble-free for many thousands of miles, excepting that there remains a small probability of failures: road hazards and driving hazards may result in a blow-out, a valve may begin to leak air, or a slow leak may develop elsewhere. Corrective maintenance, such as replacing the leaky valve and preventive maintenance, such as care to properly inflate and rotate tires at periodic intervals, can help prolong the life of the tire. Finally, however, as the tire wears bald, the battle against punctures and possible blow-outs becomes a losing one, and it is wise to make a replacement before the wear-out-failures stage sets in.

Inasmuch as wear-out failures are most readily understood from experience, their quantitative statistical nature will be examined first. Next, chance failures will be considered. Early failures will not receive extensive attention here. The testing and quality control program of a company will remove such defective products through final inspection, "debugging," "shaking-out" or "burn-in" procedures.

ANALYSIS OF WEAR-OUT FAILURES

In order to examine the statistical nature of wear-out failures, we may utilize an example of product life testing on electron tubes.

A production lot of electron tubes, especially designed to withstand high temperatures and intense vibrations, has just come off the line. A sample of 25 tubes is placed in a tray and subjected to life testing under the specified heat and vibration conditions. As each tube fails, an automatic recorder shows the time of failure. When the last of the 25 tubes has failed, the data shown on page 209 in Columns (1) to (6) are noted below. From these, it is a simple matter to derive the cumulative failure and survival percentages, as well as the Force-of-Failure data of Columns (7) to (10), supplemented by the graphic presentation of Fig. 44.

If the test was realistic in terms of the required temperatures, vibrations and other ambient conditions, then it will have yielded useful information regarding the survival characteristics of the tubes. There will be justification for a statement, based on the percentage of survivals of Column (9), as follows:

"Under actual operation, we may expect that the tubes will survive well enough so that:

92 percent will operate properly for at least 110 hours,

76 percent will operate properly for at least 120 hours, and

28 percent will operate properly for at least 130 hours, but beyond that only a few tubes will function."

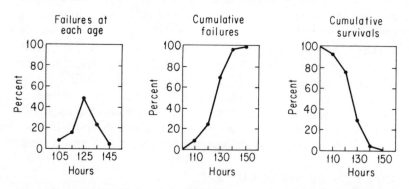

Fig. 44. Failure frequencies. First, the failure frequency at each tube age is shown. Next, these frequencies are cumulated upward, showing the percentage of tubes that failed after 110, 120, etc., hours or at a later age. Finally, a downward cumulation of failures gives, in effect, the percentage of tubes that survived at least up to the ages 110, 120, etc. hours of the base scale. The percentages of survival also represent the probability that an individual tube chosen randomly from the lot will survive to at least 110, 120, etc., hours.

Analysis of Wear-out Failures

(1) (2) Time Interval Hours in which Tubes Failed		(3) (4) Number of Good Tubes at		(5) (6) Failures during Interval		(7) (8) Cumulative Failures		(9) Cumulative Survivals	(10) Force of Failure
Start	End	Start	End	No.	%	No.	%	%	%
100	109.9	25	23	2	8	2	8	92	8
110	119.9	23	19	4	16	6	24	76	17
120	129.9	19	7	12	48	18	72	28	63
130	139.9	7	1	6	24	24	96	4	86
140	150	1	0	1	4	25	100	0	100
Totals				25	100				

Notes:

Columns (1) and (2) give the time interval in which the various tubes failed.

Columns (3) and (4) show that we started with a sample of 25 tubes. As tubes failed during each time interval of 10 hours, the number of "good" tubes surviving dwindled. Except in the first line, the start of Col. (3) is the end of Col. (4), prior line.

Columns (5) and (6) contain the number and percent of tubes failing in each time interval. The original 25 good tubes serve as the percentage base. For the second row as an example, 4 failures out of 25 tubes = $100 \times 4 \div 25 = 16$ percent.

Column (7) is cumulated by successive additions from Col. (5). For example: $0 + 2 = 2$, $2 + 4 = 6$, $6 + 12 = 18$, etc. Col. (8) is obtained similarly from Col. (6).

Column (9) represents a subtraction of Col. (8) from 100 percent.

Column (10) reveals an increasing Force of Failure, based on the relation:

$$\text{Force of Failure} = 100 \times \frac{\text{No. of Failures during Interval}}{\text{No. at start of Interval}} = 100 \times \text{Col. (5)} \div \text{Col. (3)}.$$

For example, for the second line, $100 \times 4 \div 23 = 17$ percent (rounded).

Whether or not the production lot conforms to specifications can then be evaluated in terms of the intended use of the tubes. We will examine these problems further, beginning with a consideration of how the cumulative survival percentages lead to probability and thus reliability statements.

PROBABILITY OF SURVIVAL

We have observed that 92 percent of the tubes in the sample survived for at least 110 operating hours. From this, it is our most likely expectation that this same percentage in the production lot will also survive for at least 110 hours. Moreover, it is intuitively clear that for any one tube chosen at random from the lot, the probability of survival for at least 110 hours is 92 percent. We have moved from a relative frequency to a probability statement. This approach is also consistent with the probability concepts developed in Chapter 12 and subsequent materials in this book.

True enough, we cannot say whether a given tube will have a certain length of age. In fact, a tube may survive anywhere from 100 to 150 hours. But the chances that any tube will survive at least 110 hours are 92 out of 100. Correspondingly, the risk of failure is 100—92 or 8 percent.

Reliability in terms of probability of survival is often denoted by the expression P_s, given in terms of a decimal fraction or a percentage. Thus, P_s for at least 110 hours is 92 percent or 0.92.

SHARPENING THE RELIABILITY ASSESSMENT

We have just completed a valid assessment of product reliability. Our evaluation can be sharpened, however, if we can make use of the underlying distribution of the lot for a further, somewhat more refined estimate. The normal distribution pattern of the illustrative example of the electron tubes, justifies our assuming a normal pattern for the lot itself.

There is still another reason for presuming a normal lot distribution. Experience for a large variety of products in many different industries shows that most often the observed patterns of wear-out tend to be normally distributed about the arithmetic mean of the wear-out age. Accordingly, by assuming on the basis of the available evidence that the wear-out phenomena for our electronic tube lot is normally distributed, we can reconstruct this distribution by reference to the average failure age of 125 hours and the computed standard deviation. For the latter quantity, we use the sampled data on age at time of failure as a basis, proceeding as shown in the tabulation (below).

Standard Deviation of Tube Wear-out Data

Mid-Point Failure-Time Interval[a]	Frequency of Failures[b]	Deviation from Mean[c]	Squared Deviation	Frequency × Deviation
105	2	−20	+400	800
115	4	−10	100	400
125	12	0	0	0
135	6	−10	100	600
145	1	−20	400	400
Totals	25	—	—	2200

Variance (2200/24), in hours   92[d]

Standard Deviation, $\sqrt{92}$, rounded, in hours   10

[a] Each entry is the midpoint of the 100 to 110, 110 to 120, etc., intervals in which failures are recorded.
[b] These are the same frequencies as previously given.
[c] Arithmetic mean is 125 hours.
[d] The sample size, N, is 25. Use of $N − 1 = 25 − 1$ or 24 in the divisor is a refinement of the calculation procedure, which is futher explained in Appendix I.

The standard deviation found is 10 hours. This value, together with the arithmetic mean of 125 hours, serves as the estimator of the lot characteristic. Instead of the ordinary bell-shaped normal curve, however, we shall use its cumulative form as shown in Fig. 45. This smooth curve is similar to the pattern revealed in the third graph of Fig. 44. The difference between the two is that the latter represents the sampled data as received, whereas the former is the smooth normal curve.

The vertical scale of the cumulative normal curve is expressed in terms of Probability of Survival, P_s, from 0 to 100. We realize that the 100 percent point more accurately represents 99.7 percent. The base scale is in terms of plus and minus deviations, in multiples of standard deviation, from the center of the distribution. The center represents the arithmetic mean of the data. Zero at the base scale of the cumulative normal curve is therefore that point which

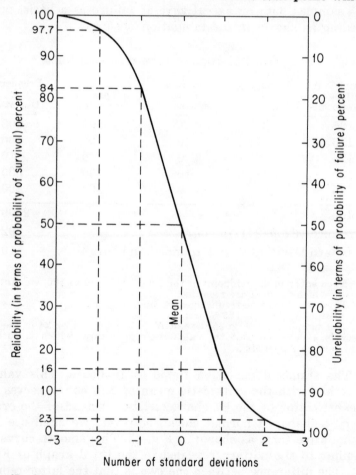

Fig. 45. Cumulative form of normal distribution curve, expressed in probability terms for use in reliability evaluations. Observe that the arithmetic average occurs at the 50 percent probability point.

corresponds to the arithmetic mean, or 125 hours in our example. The curve shows, as expected, that the probability of survival, P_s, to at least 125 hours for any tube is fifty percent. Next, the point "−1 Standard Deviations" corresponds to 125 − (1 x 10) or 115, inasmuch as σ is 10. We observe that P_s is 84 percent. Other points are obtained similarly.

By employing the normal curve for our estimations, we have smoothed the data and thus increased the precision of the method of evaluating reliability. Let us make a quick comparison. Previously, the cumulative data of Fig. 44, yielded a P_s for 110 hours' failure-free operation of 92 percent. The smoothed normal curve approach proceeds as follows:

1. The point of "at least 110 hours' survival" corresponds to 15 hours below the average of 125.
2. Show these 15 hours as −15 to indicate the "below average" position.
3. Divide −15 by the Standard Deviation of 10, giving −1.5.
4. In Fig. 45, −1.5 corresponds to 93 percent for P_s.
5. As an alternative to the graphic evaluation, refer to Table 10, which has the entry 43 at 1.5 σ. (Since the table deals with only one half of the curve, pluses and minuses are omitted). Add 50 to 43, giving 93 percent for P_s.

Although the two reliabilities of 92 and 93 percent for the original and smoothed data are quite close, as we reach farther points of the curve, the discrepancies tend to become larger. Hence it is preferable to use the smoothed curve.

ANALYSIS OF CHANCE FAILURES

Between the relatively brief phases of early failures and later wearout there is a comparatively long period of useful life of a product, during which there is usually but a small expectation of malfunction. For example, a production lot of a certain item may contain some 2 percent of the items that fail during burn-in. Next, there is a useful life of, say, 10 hours with an expectation that some 0.5 percent of the items may fail, followed by the wearout stage.

Now if 10,000 units have been burned-in, they will next be entering a useful life expectation of a total of 10,000 times 10 hours or 100,000 hours. Fifty items, representing 0.5 percent of 10,000, will fail at some time in this span. These are the chance failures. In quantitative terms we may say that the Failure Rate, denoted by a small Greek λ (lambda), is:

$$\lambda = 50 \div 100{,}000 = 0.0005 \text{ failures per hour}$$
$$\text{or 5 failures per 10,000 hours.}$$

Conversely, one may say that the average or Mean Time to Failure, designated by MTTF or more briefly by m, is

$$m = 100{,}000 \div 50 = 2000 \text{ hours.}$$

Observe that $m = 1 \div \lambda$ and $\lambda = 1 \div m$, so that $m \times \lambda$ is always 1.0 and the two expressions are the reciprocals of each other. While the illustrative example has given failure rates that seem low; in practice rates that are many times lower will often be needed. This is especially true for complex systems consisting of many thousands of components, when proper operation of all parts is critical for failure-free function of the system as a whole. The manner in which small unreliabilities of individual parts can cascade into excessive risk of system failures was previously emphasized (see page 195 "Evaluation of Mechanism Reliability").

DISTRIBUTION OF CHANCE FAILURES

The occurrence characteristics of chance failures have been studied extensively on a wide variety of products. From this work, it has been found that the "normal distribution" may be expected relatively rarely. Instead, a so-called "negative exponential distribution" can be anticipated most often. A leading specialist in reliability testing sums up the results of considerable experience:*

---

* Epstein, Benjamin, "The Exponential Distribution" in *Industrial Quality Control*, vol. xv, no. 6, December 1958, page 4. Parentheses added.

"It seems as though the exponential distribution (of chance failures) plays a role in life testing analogous to that of the normal distribution in other areas of statistics."

An exponential distribution arises whenever the force of failure remains essentially constant throughout the time period considered. The illustration below demonstrates the occurrence of chance failures in a 1500 hour period for a 1000-part lot, each part being a transistor. The Force of Failure remains constant at 10 percent, (unlike the increasing Force of Failure in normal distributions).

Each time interval shown in the transistor example represents 100 hours. For the 1000 transistors at the start, there was a total operating time of 1000 × 100 or 100,000 hours. The 100 failures then represent:

$\lambda = 100 \div 100,000 = 0.001$ failure per hour or one failure per thousand hours.

Moreover, $m = 100,000 \div 100 = 1000$ hours.

Because the Force of Failure is constant at 10 percent or 0.1 for all intervals, λ and m are 0.001 and 1000 hours, respectively, for the entire set of data. Reliability in terms of P_s is given by the cumulative percentages of Column (9) on page 216 and is graphed in Fig. 46. The pattern of the curve is characteristic of a "negative exponential" distribution. "Negative" refers to the downward sloping nature. The term "exponential" indicates how P_s is obtained. For this purpose, let us first recognize that a 10 percent Force of Failure represents also a 90 percent or 0.9 Force of Survival. Now, in the first time interval we had 100 percent survivors to start. At the end, we had 100 × 0.9 or 90 percent left. In the next interval we had 90 percent × 0.9 or 81, and in the third interval 81 × 0.9 or 73 percent left. Thus, an exponent is operating, because:

$P_s = 100 \times 0.9 \times 0.9 \times 0.9 = 100 \times 0.9^3 = 73$ percent.

Other values of P_s are found similarly, but it becomes tedious to keep multiplying for exponential results. A simpler approach it to use a standardized Exponential Curve.

Effect of Constant Force of Failure on Reliability Obtained

(1) (2) Time Interval, Hours, in which Parts Failed		(3) (4) Number of Good Parts at:		(5) (6) Failures during Interval		(7) (8) Cumulative Failures		(9) Cumulative Survivals	(10) Force of Failure
Start	End	Start	End	No.	%	No.	%	%	%
0	99.9	1000	900	100	10	100	10	90	10
100	199.9	900	810	90	9	190	19	81	10
200	299.9	810	729	81	8	271	27	73	10
300	399.9	729	656	73	7	344	34	66	10
400	499.9	656	590	66	7	410	41	59	10
500	599.9	590	531	59	6	469	47	53	10
600	699.9	531	478	53	5	522	52	48	10
700	799.9	478	430	48	5	570	57	43	10
800	899.9	430	387	43	4	613	61	39	10
900	999.9	387	348	39	4	652	65	35	10
1000	1099.9	348	313	35	3½	687	69	31	10
1100	1199.9	313	282	31	3	718	72	28	10
1200	1299.9	282	254	28	3	746	75	25	10
1300	1399.9	254	229	25	2½	771	77	23	10
1400	1500	229	206	23	2	794	79	21	10

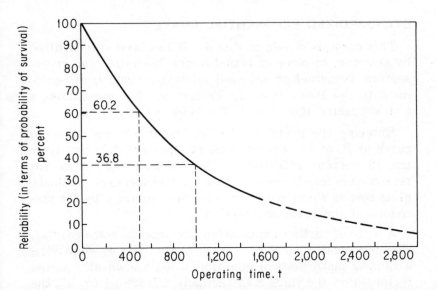

Fig. 46. Reliability curve, derived for the transistor illustration. Solid line represents demonstrated reliability, dotted line represents extrapolation.

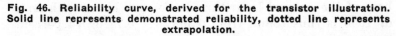

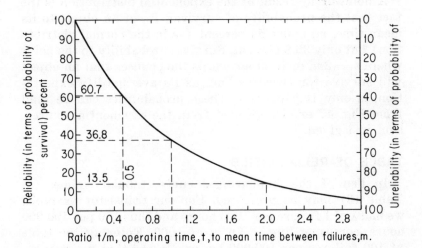

Ratio t/m, operating time, t, to mean time between failures, m.

Fig. 47. Reliability curve, based on the ratio of operating time, t, to Mean Time to Failure, m; assuming an exponential distribution (constant force of failure).

STANDARDIZED EXPONENTIAL CURVE

This curve is shown in Fig. 47. It has been standardized by showing, in place of actual hours, the ratio t/m, representing an actual or required operating time, t, of equipment to the Mean Time To Failure, m. Assuming, now, a t of 300 hours, then $t/m = 300/1000 = 0.3$.

Entering the graph at the base point 0.3, we cross the curve at P_s of 74 percent. This is 1 percent different from the 73 percent just found. The standardized curve, for reasons not easily demonstrated by elementary methods, gives results slightly more precise than obtained by the procedure of the preceding section.

A word of further explanation may interest some readers. The exponential curve of Fig. 47 is obtained by employing a famous mathematical quantity, 0.368 known also as the reciprocal of the value 2.72 (actually 2.71828+) or "e", the base of the natural logarithm. P_s for 300 hours with an m of 1000 is thus found from $0.368^{0.3} = 0.74$ or 74 percent.

A noteworthy result of the exponential distribution is the fact that the probability of survival, P_s, of an object to its mean time, m, is not 50 percent (as in the normal distribution) but only 36.8 percent. Survival probability to the point where $t = 2m$, or in other words the chances that an object will survive for twice as long as its average life expectation, is only 13.5 percent. These probabilities can be read from Fig. 47 or else gleaned from the exponential expression just given.

TABLE OF RELIABILITIES

In lieu of the standardized curve, tabular values (in Table 13) may be preferred. For our transistor example, we had λ of 1 failure per 1000 hours and thus 100 per 100,000 hours, corresponding to an m of 1000. Entering the table at 100 failures per 100,000 hours, we find that we may expect a transistor to survive at least to 100, 200, 500 or 1000 hours at these respective probabilities in percent: 90.5, 81.9, 60.7 and 36.8. The values agree closely with those obtained in the tabulated calculations previously given on page 216.

Table 13. Reliability in Terms of Probability of Survival for Various Failure Rates and Operating Times

(Based on Exponential Distribution)

Failures per 100,000 hr.	Mean Time to Failure	Hours of Operation													
		5	10	20	50	100	200	300	500	1000	2000	3000	5000	7500	10,000
		Probability, Percent, of Survival, P_s													
1	100,000	99.995	99.99	99.98	99.95	99.9	99.8	99.7	99.5	99.0	98.0	97.0	95.1	92.8	90.5
2	50,000	99.990	99.98	99.96	99.90	99.8	99.6	99.4	99.0	98.0	96.1	94.2	90.5	86.1	81.9
3	33,300	99.985	99.97	99.94	99.85	99.7	99.4	99.1	98.5	97.0	94.2	91.4	86.1	79.9	74.1
4	25,000	99.980	99.96	99.92	99.80	99.6	99.2	98.8	98.0	96.1	92.3	88.7	81.7	74.1	67.0
5	20,000	99.975	99.95	99.90	99.75	99.5	99.0	98.5	97.5	95.1	90.5	86.1	77.9	68.7	60.7
6	16,700	99.970	99.94	99.88	99.70	99.4	98.8	98.2	97.0	94.2	88.7	83.5	74.1	63.8	54.9
7	14,300	99.965	99.93	99.86	99.65	99.3	98.6	97.9	96.6	93.2	86.9	81.1	70.5	59.2	49.7
8	12,500	99.960	99.92	99.84	99.60	99.2	98.4	97.6	96.1	92.3	85.2	78.7	67.0	54.9	44.9
9	11,100	99.955	99.91	99.82	99.55	99.1	98.2	97.3	95.6	91.4	83.5	76.3	63.8	50.9	40.7
10	10,000	99.95	99.9	99.8	99.5	99.0	98.0	97.0	95.1	90.5	81.9	74.1	60.7	47.2	36.8
20	5,000	99.90	99.8	99.6	99.0	98.0	96.1	94.2	90.5	81.9	67.0	54.9	36.8	22.3	13.5
30	3,330	99.85	99.7	99.4	98.5	97.0	94.2	91.4	86.1	74.1	54.9	40.7	22.3	10.5	5.0
40	2,500	99.80	99.6	99.2	98.0	96.1	92.3	88.7	81.9	67.0	44.9	30.1	13.5	5.0	1.8
50	2,000	99.75	99.5	99.0	97.5	95.1	90.5	86.1	77.9	60.7	36.8	22.3	8.2	2.4	0.7
60	1,670	99.70	99.4	98.8	97.0	94.2	88.7	83.5	74.1	54.9	30.1	16.5	5.0	1.1	0.3
70	1,430	99.65	99.3	98.6	96.6	93.2	86.9	81.1	70.5	49.7	24.7	12.3	3.0	0.5	0.1
80	1,250	99.60	99.2	98.4	96.1	92.3	85.2	78.7	67.0	44.9	20.2	9.1	1.8	0.3	
90	1,110	99.55	99.1	98.2	95.6	91.4	83.5	76.3	63.8	40.7	16.5	6.7	1.1	0.1	
100	1,000	99.5	99.0	98.0	95.1	90.5	81.9	74.1	60.7	36.8	13.5	5.0	0.7		
200	500	99.0	98.0	96.1	90.5	81.9	67.0	54.9	36.8	13.5	1.8	0.3			
300	333	98.5	97.0	94.2	86.1	74.1	54.9	40.7	22.3	5.0	0.3				
400	250	98.0	96.1	92.3	81.9	67.0	44.9	30.1	13.5	1.8					
500	200	97.5	95.1	90.5	77.9	60.7	36.8	22.3	8.2	0.7					
600	167	97.0	94.2	88.7	74.1	54.9	30.2	16.6	5.0	0.3					
700	143	96.6	93.2	86.9	70.5	49.7	24.7	12.3	3.0	0.1					
800	125	96.1	92.3	85.2	67.0	44.9	20.2	9.1	1.8						
900	111	95.6	91.4	83.5	63.7	40.7	16.5	6.7	1.1						
1000	100	95.1	90.5	81.9	60.7	36.8	13.5	5.0	0.7						

Note: In place of hours, any time unit may be used, so long as the units are alike for the 3 terms involved: Average number of failures per period (λ); Mean time to (or between) failure(s) (m); and operating time (t). In place of a time period, a time-related basis may also be used, such as "number of actuations" or "number of flexures" until failure. For example, relay life might be expressed in terms of failure-free actuations and wire life may be measured by the number of flexures that the wire can withstand before breaking.

The example also permits a further check of the expression $0.368^{t/m}$. Thus, a survival time t of 500 hours yields a t/m of $500/1000 = \frac{1}{2}$. But a number raised to the half power is its square root. The square root of 0.368 is 0.607 corresponding to the 60.7 percent above. When t is 2000, t/m becomes 2, and the square of 0.368 is 0.135, which corresponds to the entry $P_s = 13.5$ percent under $t = 2000$ of the table. When t is 1000, t/m is 1, so that $0.368^1 = 0.368 = 36.8$ percent as above.

A valuable further application of the table is apparent. Suppose, that we had checked the transistors for only 100 hours, observing a Force of Failure of 10 percent, from which m is then found to be 1000. So long as we can reasonably expect the Force of Failure to be constant, we can make reliability predictions for survival of any transistor to 200, 500, 1000, 2000, or 3000 hours or more, using merely the ratio t/m. The exponential curve that started out as a theoretical discussion has thus become a practical tool for evaluation and prediction of reliability.

REPAIRABLE AND NON-REPAIRABLE FAILURES

The concept of Mean Time To Failure, MTTF, or m for short has been used with regard to equipment that for economic or practical reasons is not repairable, such as an orbiting satellite. When repairs are expected, however, we use MTBF, Mean Time Between Failures. Both terms are designated by the shorter symbol, m, since they are used in identical manner in entering Fig. 47 or Table 13.

Many objects are both repairable and non-repairable. A missile on the launching pad is repairable; in flight it is not. Yet, the value of m will differ for either stage. For the flight-stage there will be far greater environmental punishment, such as shock, vibration and temperature, so that MTTF will be poorer than MTBT. Also, some components may not be needed during either the ground or the flight phase, thus compounding the differences. In practice, all of these factors must be considered in order to answer the question: "Will this thing work, and for how long?"

Consider an electronic guidance system. Installed in a sea-going vessel, it may have an MTBT of 1000 hours. From Table 13, we find that P_s for 1,000 hours is 36.8 percent. Obviously, this is a rather poor reliability. But there is a 95.1 percent probability for the system to operate properly for at least 50 hours. We may accept the guidance system under the provision that preventive maintenance occurs approximately every 50 hours of actual use. If this maintenance succeeds in removing parts—resistors, transistors, tubes,—that have tended to drift towards limiting performance values, thus correcting incipient trouble spots, then there will in fact prevail a 95.1 percent reliability.

Installed in a plane, however, the system is exposed to greater environmental stresses. Its MTBF may deteriorate by a factor of 2, so that MTBF becomes 500 hours. P_s for 1000 is now only 13.5 percent and P_s for 50 hours is 90.5. The system may be rejected as inadequate. For the sake of illustration, however, assume that this same system is now being considered for a missile. Here the stresses are so considerable, that instead of an m of 1000 or 500, we have an m of but 100. P_s for 50 hours' survival has become 60.7 percent, and the m now refers to MTTF. But the missile may have to function for only 5 hours,* in which case P_s becomes 95.1. An odd situation has developed. The component that was unsuitable for aircraft has become adequate for a missile. But usually the shoe is on the other foot: The more demanding an environment is, the more difficult the attainment of suitable products to meet requirements.

PRACTICAL VALUE OF RELIABILITY INFORMATION

Availability of data regarding m and P_s is of considerable benefit to management in many situations, such as the following:

Maintenance. Knowledge of the life expectancy and wear-out characteristics of component parts of equipment, with

---

* Since a missile can cover half the globe in only 0.5 hour, the required 5 hours may seem unrealistic. In practice, however, designers of missiles and other complex and critical devices usually allow for a safety factor. In this case a safety factor of 10 would raise the 0.5 hours to 5 hours.

estimates of the time interval in which equipment may fail, leads to the development of (1) sound maintenance frequencies and (2) appropriate provision for spare parts, stand-by equipment and replacements.

Maintainability plus reliability affect equipment availability. For example, if Mean Time Between Failures is 200 hours and it takes 50 hours to repair and maintain equipment for this time interval, then equipment availability is $200/(200 + 50) = 80$ percent.

Mission Success. Assessment of reliability permits evaluation of the success likelihood of a mission. Appropriate action can then be taken. For example, if the probability of success of a single space probe to a distant planet is considered inadequate, one may be able to improve the chances of overall success by dispatching two probes. For other purposes, such as a manned flight, equipment may be rejected until it has been re-designed to be suitable.

Cost Control. It is possible to correlate product reliability requirements with product costs. The quality of components used is then matched with the needs specified. Thus, a transistor going into a television set can be produced to a much lower price than a transistor going into a missile. Reliability analysis ascertains the degree of reliability needed for each purpose.

Safety. Only by knowing reliability of components can equipment be built for maximum attainable safety.

Evaluation of reliability thus becomes an important engineering and management tool, without which the age of space travel, computerization and automation would be unthinkable; but which is equally applicable to the home appliance and automobile.

23

Reliability Assurance

Having discussed the fundamental concepts in assessing reliability, we must now turn our attention to a further vital aspect: How do we assure that products have the required degree of reliability for their intended mission? Engineering proof of such reliability must be marshalled in order to support reliability statements.

RELIABILITY TESTING

Assurance of reliability begins with reliability testing. One type of such testing has already been discussed. Sample pieces of product, selected randomly from a production lot or other rational group, are subjected to life testing. The number of failures are recorded together with the age at failure. The electron tube and the transistor examples represent such types of effort. In many practical situations, however, it is not feasible from a standpoint of time, manpower, testing facilities and costs to make extensive observations.

Abbreviated Life Tests. On many types of products, the characteristic force-of-failure pattern can be predicted with reasonable validity. When we are dealing with chance failures and thus a constant force of failure the data of Table 13 will properly predict reliability on the basis of a brief initial test.

Failure-Repair Runs. Although an item may be non-repairable in actual application, it is often feasible to repair failures during reliability testing. Fewer test units will thus be needed since a repaired item can be looked at as a "new" unit; or else the value of MTBF of testing can be considered an MTTF for end-use purposes.

Accelerated Tests. Ingenious ways of accelerated testing to compress time have been found. One way is to change time, such as hours, to some other criterion, such as number of actuations. For example, instead of testing a snap-action thermostat for 2 years, we can rig up a device which through rapid temperature changes causes many tens of thousands of "on" and "off" actuations in a few days. The failures observed are now MTTF in terms of number of actuations rather than hours, but Table 13 and Figure 47 will be equally valid. We can also convert the actuations observed to hours. For example, if in its end use a thermostat has an average of 10 actuations per hour, then a MTTF of 100,000 actuations corresponds to 10,000 hours of operation.

Test of Increased Severity. Sometimes it is possible to increase the severity of the required temperatures, vibrations, current strengths and other stresses on a test specimen or device. If the item does not fail during relatively brief exposure to these intensified factors, extrapolations can be made to predict the life of the object under lesser but prolonged periods of stress. Because of the complexities and pitfalls in such extrapolations, the approach must be employed with great care and circumspection.

Tests of Large Sample Sizes. Instead of testing a few items to destruction, we can test many items until a few have failed. For example, instead of testing 10 capacitors until they fail; we can test 100 of them until 10 have failed. The time savings accomplished are significant, but the costs of sampling large numbers of units are often considerable.

The last mentioned approach requires the application of a sampling table, as will be discussed next.

APPLICATION OF SAMPLING TABLE

The use of the sampling plans in Table 14 requires an illustrative example. Assume that a shipment of transistors has been received, and that a mean life of 10,000 hours has been specified. Only about 200 hours are available for testing. The ratio of this testing time, 200, to the specified mean life, 10,000, is 0.02. Entering the Table for this column, we find that if a sample of 116 resistors is tested for 200 hours and zero failures occur, we can be 90 percent confident that the shipment as a whole conforms to the specified mean life of 10,000 hours.

Statistically, this is a sound approach. But if one failure is found, calling for a rejection of the lot, we might receive squawks from the supplier. "After all, one failure is possible even under good production," he may claim. So, we may decide that we need to find at least 2 failures for rejection, meaning that for acceptance up to 1 failure is permissible. But, as the table shows, our sample size now increases to 195, and the practical inspector, engineer and manager may be dismayed at this relatively large sample size. Lot-by-lot acceptance of products that must meet stringent requirements is indeed a costly business in terms of materials, manpower and testing time.

Table 14. Sample Sizes Needed for Reliability Testing

Acceptance No.	Ratio of Testing to Specified Mean Life												
	1.0	0.5	0.2	0.1	0.05	0.02	0.01	0.005	0.002	0.001	0.0005	0.0002	0.0001
	Sample Size, No. of Units												
0	3	5	12	24	47	116	231	461	1,152	2,303	4,606	11,513	23,026
1	5	9	20	40	79	195	390	778	1,946	3,891	7,780	19,450	38,898
2	7	12	28	55	109	266	533	1,065	2,662	5,323	10,645	26,612	53,223
3	9	15	35	69	137	333	668	1,337	3,341	6,681	13,362	33,404	66,808
4	11	19	42	83	164	398	798	1,599	3,997	7,994	15,988	39,968	79,936
5	13	22	49	97	190	462	927	1,855	4,638	9,275	18,549	46,374	92,747
6	15	25	56	110	217	528	1,054	2,107	5,267	10,533	21,064	52,661	105,322
7	16	28	63	123	243	589	1,178	2,355	5,886	11,771	23,542	58,855	117,710
8	18	31	70	136	269	648	1,300	2,599	6,498	12,995	25,990	64,974	129,948
9	20	34	76	149	294	709	1,421	2,842	7,103	14,206	28,412	71,030	142,060
10	22	37	83	161	319	770	1,541	3,082	7,704	15,407	30,814	77,034	154,068
11	23	40	89	174	344	830	1,660	3,320	8,300	16,598	33,197	82,991	165,982
12	25	42	95	187	369	888	1,779	3,557	8,891	17,782	35,564	88,908	177,816
13	27	45	102	199	393	947	1,896	3,792	9,479	18,958	37,916	94,790	189,580
14	29	48	108	212	417	1,007	2,013	4,026	10,064	20,128	40,256	100,640	201,280

Notes:

1. Entries show the minimum sample size that must be tested for the length of time shown, to assure a mean life (MTTF or MTBF) of at least the length required, with a confidence of 90 percent that this mean life actually prevails in the lot accepted.

2. Table is based on exponential failure distribution.

Source: Sobel, M. and Tischendorf, J. A., Proceedings of Fifth National Symposium, Reliability Quality Control, IRE January 1959, pp. 108-118.

SEQUENTIAL SAMPLING PLANS

It is also possible to employ the sequential sampling plans of Table 1, pages 10 and 11. Assume, for example, that a shipment of 2000 flashlight batteries has been received. The specification states that any battery must have a life of at least 3 hours, and that the Allowable Percent Defective shall be no more than 5.0. The table shows that our first sequential sample must consist of 50 units. If none fail, the lot is accepted. If 6 fail the lot is rejected. For 1 to 5 failures, further sampling is called for. The procedure has been described in detail in Chapter 2, and the sampling risks involved were discussed in Chapter 12.

PRACTICAL RELIABILITY ASSURANCE

This chapter has been concerned with the principal aspects of reliability assurance, i.e., with the testing of products for reliability in accordance with specified requirements. In presenting methods of sampling and testing, attention was also called to necessary precautions in interpreting test results. A comprehensive assurative testing program must rely on many tools:

1. Complete descriptions of the products that are required to undergo reliability testing. These descriptions will include specifications for both quality and reliability.
2. Concise prescriptions for the performance of tests, including meticulous attention to the ambient conditions—such as number of operating cycles and times, temperatures, shock, pressures and vibrations—that are to prevail during testing.
3. Definitely laid down sampling procedures, sample sizes, criteria for judging the success or failure of an item and acceptance and rejection values for action on a lot.
4. Knowledge of the calculated sampling risks, such as embodied in operating characteristic curves or tabulated data on the probabilities of sampling errors.

It will often be impractical to subject a large and complex system to performance testing. There will, however, be data on component reliabilities. Fortunately, it is possible to synthesize from these individual probabilities the expected reliability of the system as a whole, as will be shown in the next chapter.

In reliability assurance, just as in quality control, we thus observe that a sound program provides for strategic testing at various stages of production. When such testing occurs, we may at times be at a loss in properly defining it. For example, is a check of tensile strength of a critical structural part a quality control or a reliability assurance test? From a practical viewpoint, we resolve this problem by observing that reliability is but one—albeit a most important—characteristic of good product quality. Indeed, installation of reliability assurance often has been most successful in those organizations that have already had a good quality control program, with detailed quality assurance procedures,[1] in effect.

---

[1] For illustrative examples see Covino, C. P. and A. W. Meghri, *Quality Assurance Manual*, The Industrial Press, New York.

24

Reliability Design

Important as such assurative activities as reliability testing and evaluation are, they cannot enhance the ultimate soundness of the product itself. Accordingly, a great deal of emphasis in reliability engineering has been placed on the reliability inherent in the design itself. In turn, the statistical methods of reliability analysis aid the design-engineer in his work, by predicting the reliability to be expected from various alternatives designs. On the basis of these predictions, an optimal decision can then be made.

Precision of predictions is essential, otherwise inadequate or over-designed product may result. An inadequate door-hinge will invite complaints and returns from premature failures, while an over-designed hinge may incur undue costs of heavy-gauge steel, corrosion-resistant alloys and excessive machining, thus pricing the product outside the market. In space craft, problems of precise reliability prediction become critical. Under-designed components may be catastrophic while over-design may bring burdensome problems of weight and complexity.

RELIABILITY IMPROVEMENT THROUGH REDUNDANCY

The non-redundant system in Figure 48 consists of three elements; a transmitter, a receiver, and a coder. The probabilities of failure-free operation for 100 hours of this system depend on the component reliabilities.

Using the symbol P_s to indicate "Probability of successful operation" for the time interval of 100 hours, we observe these component or element reliabilities:

P_s (Transmitter) $= P_s$ (T) $= 70$ Percent or 0.70
P_s (Receiver) $= P_s$ (R) $= 90$ Percent or 0.90
P_s (Coder) $= P_s$ (C) $= 80$ Percent or 0.80

We read P_s (Transmitter) as "Probability of success of transmitter" in sending out the message. Similar reading applies to all other such uses of the parentheses after a probability statement.

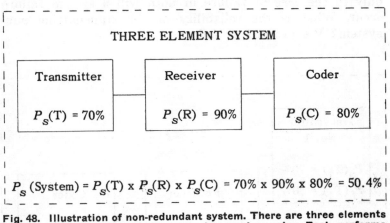

Fig. 48. Illustration of non-redundant system. There are three elements in the system; a transmitter, a receiver and a coder. Each performs its specific function, and there is no duplication of these functions.

It is apparent that the reliability of the system hinges on the proper operation of all three elements. Failure of one defeats the entire system. Therefore,

P_s (System) $= P_s$ (T) $\times P_s$ (R) $\times P_s$ (C)
$= 0.70 \times 0.90 \times 0.80 = 0.504$
$= 50$ Percent, approximately.

The reader will rightly observe that this is a relatively poor reliability. Indeed, for purposes of simplified arithmetic the example has involved rounded, rather low reliabilities. A more realistic set of reliabilities would have been 0.97, 0.99 and 0.98 in place of the three probabilities just given. However, even with those higher values, the P_s of the system would be only $0.97 \times 0.99 \times 0.98$ or 94 percent, which may be considered inadequate for many

purposes. Assuming that the reliability of each element
cannot be improved, then by utilizing one or more extra
or duplicating components—that is, the inclusion of redundancy—we might enhance overall system reliability.
Let us see how this works.

Duplication of one element, such as the transmitter,
would represent an instance of redundancy, as shown in
Figure 49. The two transmitters are in parallel, so that
only in the case of failure of both will a system failure
occur. What is the reliability of the transmitting sub-
system? We proceed as follows:

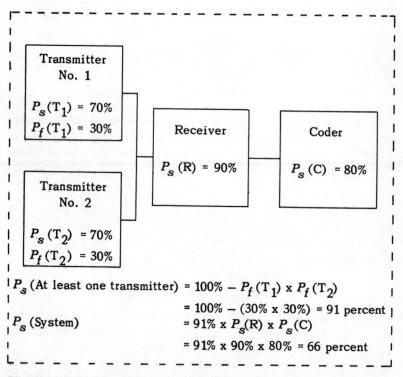

Fig. 49. Illustration of redundant system. The prior 3-element system
has been enlarged to include a duplication of the transmitting function.
Two transmitters are now in the system, operating in parallel: If one
transmitter fails, the other may still work. The receiver and coder
are in series. If either fails or if both transmitters fail, the system is
inoperative.

1. Since the sub-system can only be in one of two states, "successful operation" or "failure," the two probabilities of P_s and P_f must total to 1.0 or 100 percent.
2. The probability of a failure, P_f, of either transmitter is 0.3 or 30 percent. Therefore, the chance that both will fail is 0.3×0.3 or 0.09 = 9 percent.
3. Subtraction of this 0.09 from 1.00 gives P_s of 0.91 or 91 percent for the transmitting sub-system.

The sub-system, in turn, is in series with the receiver and the coder. For the system as a whole, therefore, we have:

$$P_s \text{ (System)} = P_s \text{ (Sub-system)} \times P_s \text{ (R)} \times P_s \text{ (C)}$$
$$= 0.91 \times 0.90 \times 0.80 = 0.655$$
$$= 66 \text{ percent.}$$

Redundancy has increased overall system reliability from the original 50 to a 66 percent reliability. Further improvements may be possible, through receiver and coder duplication, or through employment of three rather than just two elements in parallel. The price for increased reliability through redundancy will be in terms of the extra cost of the duplication of facilities. Complexity of the system as a whole may increase even further, such as when "fail-safe" devices are required that automatically switch operations from failing to working elements in a sub-system.

RELIABILITY IN SINGLE- AND DOUBLE-LIMIT OPERATIONS

In the prediction of reliability of the transmitter-receiver-coder system, we were concerned with only one possible type of failure: an element might not function when required. This is a single-limit type of failure. A double-limit operation involves two types of malfunction. Take, for example, a switch. There is always a possibility that because of "stickiness" or a weak spring or other reasons, the switch might fail to close when required. There is, however, also a second type of malfunction. The switch might close prematurely. A slightly loose assembly, affected by further stresses of low temperatures, jarring and rapid acceleration, might cause a switch to shut when no closure of a circuit is intended. Thus, there are two types of failure: non-closure and premature closure.

If, instead of a switch we had been dealing with a valve, we might again be facing two types of possible failures: Non-closure of a flow of liquid in a fuel system or premature shutting off of the flow. A variety of instances of two-sided failures can occur in most complex systems. A 3-sided failure mode involves, for example, an explosive fuze that (1) might not light, (2) might light prematurely, (3) might explode on lighting.

In the design of equipment, it is essential that proper consideration be given to the types of failure that can occur, since each type might have a different significance. For example, a switching fault that causes a premature firing of a missile may be worse than a failure to fire.

REDUNDANCY AND RELIABILITY OF DOUBLE-LIMIT OPERATIONS

A large-scale system contains an element which is placed into action by the closure of a circuit between the points "a" and "b" of the diagram in Figure 50. Experience has shown that a certain type of switch has a reliability of 70 percent of at least 1000 proper closures. Considering this probability inadequate, we have placed two identical types of switches, A and B, in parallel. As a result (see calculation in Fig. 50), the reliability of the switching system has been increased to 77 percent.

At the same time, the likelihood that a switch might fail to close, P_f, which is 20 percent for a single unit, has decreased to $(0.20)^2 = 4$ percent for the combination. Unfortunately, however, premature closure has increased from $P_p = 10$ percent for one switch to $P_p = 19$ percent for the two switches in parallel. If premature closure is a potentially serious hazard in terms of safety and costs, then redundancy has certainly not improved matters where it counts most heavily.

Another design, in Figure 51, employs four switches, which reduces the premature failure possibilities. But we

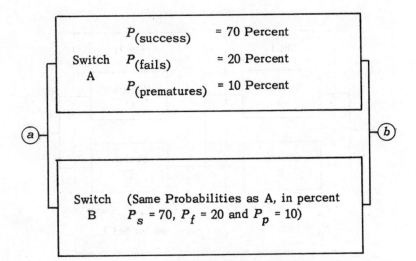

$P_{(success)}$ = 70 Percent

Switch $P_{(fails)}$ = 20 Percent

A

$P_{(prematures)}$ = 10 Percent

(a)   (b)

Switch   (Same Probabilities as A, in percent

B P_s = 70, P_f = 20 and P_p = 10)

CALCULATION OF RELIABILITIES

| Possible Outcomes | | Probabilities of Outcomes, Percent | | | | System |
Switch A	Switch B	Switch A	Switch B	Calculations	Result	Probability
Success	Success	P_s	P_s	70 x 70	49	
Success	Failure	P_s	P_f	70 x 20		Success
Failure	Success	P_f	P_s	20 x 70	28	
Failure	Failure	P_f	P_f	20 x 20	4*	Non-closure
Success	Premature	P_s	P_p	70 x 10		
Premature	Success	P_p	P_s	10 x 70	14**	
Failure	Premature	P_f	P_p	20 x 10		Premature
Premature	Failure	P_p	P_f	10 x 20	4**	Closure
Premature	Premature	P_p	P_p	10 x 10	1**	
All (total)					100	

*Probability of Failure to Close is 4 Percent for the System.
**Probability of Premature Closure is 14 + 4 + 1 = 19 Percent for the System.
  Therefore, System Reliability is 100 — 4 — 19 = 77 Percent.

Fig. 50. Reliability of a set of parallel switches. While the probability of non-closure, P_f, is less than for a single switch (4 vs. 20 percent), the likelihood of premature closure, P_p has increased (from 10 to 19 percent).

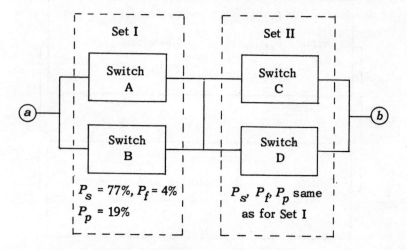

CALCULATION OF RELIABILITIES

Possible Outcomes		Probabilities of Outcomes, Percent				System
Set I	Set II	Set I	Set II	Calculations	Result	Probability
Success	Success	P_s	P_s	77 x 77	59	Success
Premature	Premature	P_p	P_p	19 x 19	4	Premature Closure
Failure	Failure	—	—	100 − 59 − 4	37	Non-closure
Total					100	

Notes: Sets I and II may be considered "subsystems" of the new system of two pairs of switches.

The probability of successful closure of the system, P_s, is derived from the individual probabilities, P_s, of each set of switches. Similarly for the probability, P_p of premature closure of the system.

The probability, P_f, that the arrangement of switches will fail to close the system can be derived indirectly, by subtracting P_s and P_p of the system, 59 and 4 percent respectively, from 100 percent, thus yielding a system P_f of 37 percent.

Fig. 51. Reliability of 2 sets of parallel switches, arranged as shown here. Each set of switches has the reliabilities previously calculated for the single set of switches in parallel.

may now be dissatisfied with the increase in the probability of non-closure. Possible designs thus far considered involve these probabilities:

Reliability and
Failure Probability Percentages

	One Switch Only	Two Switches in Parallel	Four-Switch Arrangement
Successful closure	70	77	59
Failure to close	20	4	37
Premature closure	10	19	4

Redundancy, obviously, is not an unmixed blessing. It is precisely this fact, however, which makes analysis and prediction of reliability so important. With this statistical technique, we can inform ourselves of the relative merits of several possible designs. One can then choose the optimum of a set of alternative designs. As a still further possibility, we might develop additional and probably more complex designs. Whether or not such action is needed depends on the exigencies of the missions envisioned for the equipment and the resources in terms of time, money and manpower available.

PRACTICAL RELIABILITY-REDUNDANCY STUDIES

In practical reliability prediction of various possible product designs, we must recognize a number of precautionary aspects:

1. Parallel redundancy cannot be taken for granted. Equipment is often arranged in parallel, but operates as though in series. Capacitors are a prime example. They may be wired parallel but act in series in the sense that failure of either one of the two capacitors will cause malfunction of the system depending on them.

2. Combination of reliabilities depends on proper time bases. In the transmitter-receiver-coder example, as a case in point, each P_s value was based on like time values of 100 hours of operation. In many systems, however, it may be found that various elements work for only a part of the entire system's operating life. Proper cognizance of time bases must then be taken.

In summary, a combination of engineering knowledge of components plus a statistical assembly of probabilities are the ingredients that jointly guide us to valid reliability predictions. Once these practical precautions have been observed, wide applicability will be found for the methods shown here, regardless of whether a large-scale system, a sub-system or merely an assembly is analyzed. Any configuration of basic elements is predictable, once the individual reliabilities are known.

CONVERSION OF TIME BASES

It has been emphasized that time bases for reliability figures must be comparable. For example, assume that a radar defense installation includes two systems: a search unit and a tracking unit. The first must operate continuously, the second only ten percent of the time. Assume now that, based on 1000 hours, we have these reliabilities.

Search radar unit, $P_s = 90.5$ percent
Tracking radar unit, $P_s = 40.7$ percent

The tracking radar, however, is needed only for 100 hours out of every 1000 hours of search. For 900 hours it is silent. Converting P_s (1000 hours) $= 40.7$ percent to the more applicable P_s (100 hours) we find a probability of 91.4 percent. The value is obtained from Table 13 in Chapter 22, using the 1000 and 100 operating hour columns at the level of 90 failures per 100,00 hours.

What is the probability that both search and tracking radar units will function when needed?

Search $P_s = 0.905$
Tracking $P_s = 0.914$
P_s (System) $= 0.905 \times 0.914 = 0.827$

We thus expect an 82.7 percent probability that, when both radar units are needed, they will both be operating properly. In practice, the defense of the installation may also require proper functioning of a computer, launchers, guidance systems and missiles. The addition of these elements in the reliability calculation will again require comparable time values and probabilities.

COMPONENT RELIABILITY DATA

The reader may ask: "How do we know the reliability of the basic components involved?" In practice, a large scale system is built up from many items, such as steel, plastic and electronic parts. Effective prediction of system reliability depends on valid data on components reliabilities. Many sources of information are available, compiled by trade, scientific and technical groups and by the Government.

Information has been obtained both by laboratory life tests and by gathering data on failure of equipment and parts in the field. Furthermore, within a company, information accumulates continually pertaining to the reliability of the components or other building blocks that are critical for proper functioning of equipments and other systems.

Admittedly, there is a flaw in the use of published reliability data. For example, failure rates for a certain type of transformer have been given as 20 per 100,000 hours, corresponding to a mean time between failures of 5000 hours. But this information may not be applicable to the transformers supplied by a given sub-contractor. Moreover, the failure rate may also depend on the quality of preventive maintenance in the field. As a result, the "average quality of maintenance" and the "average quality of transformer" assumed in the published failure rates may be inadequate. In time, however, as unreliable suppliers become known and are avoided and as inadequate maintenance practices are uncovered and remedied, a gradual improvement or so-called "reliability growth" will occur. Included in this growth will be the discovery within a manufacturing plant of components, design factors, use-factors, and other critical items in need of review, revision and improvement.

CONCLUDING OBSERVATIONS

Created by the needs of the space age, the concept of reliability presents an important extension in the definition of product quality. Reliability has the virtue of being expressible in quantitative terms. Products can be tested for conformance to these requirements. Designs can be analyzed with a view to the components and arrangements needed to satisfy a particular end use.

Most of the applications of reliability work have come from military and space exploration activities. But the impact on commercial products has been noted. The life of appliances, the potency of pharmaceuticals, the stability of chemicals, and the performance of synthetic heart valves are all areas where reliability is of utmost importance. The next years will, undoubtedly, see vast extensions not only of the concepts and methods of reliability but also of the fields of application.

By its nature, reliability involves a probabilistic and thus uncertain type of prediction of performance characteristics. We can hope to reduce the risks of error in such predictions, but we can not expect to ever attain certainty. Unavoidable as some allowance for error may have to be, the alternative of making no estimates, no evaluations and no predictions, is unthinkable in a modern society that is increasingly geared towards complexity of its appliances, equipment and productive machinery.

APPENDIX I

METHODS OF COMPUTING STANDARD DEVIATIONS

For most practical purposes, the standard deviation of a production lot or process may be estimated by use of the method of average ranges shown in this book. There are, however, occasions when it is desired to make more precise determinations, using direct computations. Several methods are available for this purpose, of which the most commonly used are described here. They have been placed here, in the Appendix, since they are applied less frequently than the range methods in quality control work.

BASIC METHOD

The basic method of computing standard deviations is shown in Appendix 1A. The procedure illustrated by Figure 22, page 112, represents an expansion of the basic method, for use in frequency distributions.

APPENDIX 1A

BASIC METHOD OF COMPUTING STANDARD DEVIATION

(Example of Tensile Strength Determinations)

Tensile Strength, Pounds	Average	Deviation from Average	Deviation from Average, Squared
(X)	$(\overline{X})$	$(X - \overline{X})$	$(X - \overline{X})^2$
64	62	+2	4
60	62	−2	4
62	62	0	0
66	62	+4	16
58	62	−4	16
Totals 310	—	0	40

1. Average, $\overline{X} = \dfrac{\Sigma X}{N} = \dfrac{310}{5} = 62*$

2. Variance, $\sigma^2 = \Sigma(X-\overline{X})^2/N = 40/5 = 8$

3. Standard Deviation, $\sigma = \sqrt{\sigma^2} = \sqrt{8} = 2.828$

*Σ = "Sum of," N = Sample Size.

UNBIASED METHOD

When it is desired to estimate the standard deviation of a production lot or process from a small sample, the basic method shown in Appendix 1A usually underestimates the true standard deviation slightly. In order to correct for this bias, the sample size N in the formula for the variance is replaced by N-1. The latter expression is called "Degrees of Freedom." Appendix 1B shows the method. Obviously, as the sample size becomes larger, the difference between N and N-1 becomes less important. For this reason, many texts use simply N in place of N-1 when the sample size exceeds 25 or 30. This was also done in Figure 22, page 112.

APPENDIX 1B

ESTIMATING STANDARD DEVIATION OF A LOT FROM A SAMPLE

(**Example of Tensile Strength Determinations**)

Tensile Strength, Pounds	Average	Deviation from Average	Deviation from Average, Squared
(X)	$(\overline{X})$	$(X - \overline{X})$	$(X - \overline{X})^2$
64	62	+2	4
60	62	−2	4
62	62	0	0
66	62	+4	16
58	62	−4	16
Totals 310	—	0	40

1. Average, $\overline{X}, = \dfrac{\Sigma X}{N} = \dfrac{310}{5} = 62$

2. Variance, $\sigma^2 = \Sigma(X-\overline{X})^2/(N-1) = 40/4 = 10$

3. Standard Deviation, $\sigma = \sqrt{\sigma^2} = \sqrt{10} = 3.162$

SHORT-CUT METHOD

In those cases where a desk calculator is available, and also when using electronic computers, it is preferable to use the short-cut method demonstrated in Appendix 1C. The answer should be identical to that found by the method of Appendix 1B.

APPENDIX 1C

ESTIMATING STANDARD DEVIATION OF A PRODUCTION LOT FROM A SAMPLE—SHORT CUT METHOD OF COMPUTATION

(Example of Tensile Strength Determinations)

Tensile Strength, Pounds	Strength Squared
(X)	$(X)^2$
64	4,096
60	3,600
62	3,844
66	4,356
58	3,364
Totals 310	19,260

1. $(\Sigma X)^2 = (310)^2 = 96,100$

2. Average, $\overline{X} = \dfrac{\Sigma X}{N} = \dfrac{310}{5} = 62$

3. $N = 5;\ N - 1 = 4;\ N(N-1) = 20$

4. Variance, $\sigma^2 = \dfrac{\Sigma(X)^2}{N-1} - \dfrac{(\Sigma X)^2}{N(N-1)} =$

$$= \dfrac{19,260}{4} - \dfrac{96,100}{20}$$

$$= 4,815 - 4,805 = 10$$

5. Standard Deviation, $\sigma = \sqrt{\sigma^2} = \sqrt{10} = 3.162$

GROUPED DATA

When data are grouped in the form of a frequency distribution, the computations by means of the short-cut and unbiased method proceed as illustrated in Appendix 1D. This is the fastest procedure for grouped data.

APPENDIX 1D

ESTIMATING STANDARD DEVIATION OF A LOT FROM A SAMPLE—SHORT-CUT METHOD OF COMPUTATION FOR GROUPED DATA

(Example of Product Weight)

Product Weight (oz.)	Midvalue (oz.)	Frequency (f)	Deviation* (d)	f × d = fd	fd × d = fd²
1.1-1.19	1.15	2	−3	−6	18
1.2-1.29	1.25	2	−2	−4	8
1.3-1.39	1.35	4	−1	−4	4
1.4-1.49	1.45	6	0	0	0
1.5-1.59	1.55	3	+1	+3	3
1.6-1.69	1.65	1	+2	+2	4
1.7-1.80	1.75	2	+3	+6	18
Totals	—	20		−3	55

1. Average, $\overline{X} = A + \dfrac{\Sigma(fd) \times i}{N} = 1.45 + \dfrac{-3 \times 0.1}{20} = 1.435$

2. Variance, $\sigma^2 = \left[\dfrac{\Sigma fd^2}{N-1} - \dfrac{(\Sigma fd)^2}{N(N-1)} \right] \times i$

    $= \left[\dfrac{55}{19} - \dfrac{(-3)^2}{20 \times 19} \right] \times 0.1 = .287$

3. Standard Deviation $= \sqrt{\sigma^2} = \sqrt{.287} = .5357$

---

*Deviations are measured in full class interval units, from a tentatively assumed average, A. In this example, A was taken at 1.45. The class interval units, i, are the differences between successive midvalues, representing 0.1 oz. each. For example, 1.25 − 1.15 = 0.1.

INDEX

243